STEAM-ENGINE BUILDERS OF
LINCOLNSHIRE

Steam-Engine Builders
of Lincolnshire

RONALD H. CLARK

M. I. Mech. E.
Past President of the Newcomen Society

The Society for
Lincolnshire History and Archaeology

LINCOLN

1998

Original published by Goose and Son Limited, 1955

This reprinted edition published in 1998 by:
The Society for Lincolnshire History and Archaeology
Jews' Court, Steep Hill, Lincoln, LN2 1LS

British Library Cataloguing-in-Publication Data.
A CIP catalogue record for this book is available
from the British Library.

ISBN 0-903582-12-0

Design of jacket and additional pages by
The S S Crome, Alford, Lincolnshire.

Printed in the UK by Henry Ling Limited, Dorchester.

PREFACE TO THE REPRINTED EDITION

AT LAST we have a reprint of Ronald Clark's valuable illustrated catalogue of some of the many fascinating engineering firms that have made Lincolnshire a leading county in the development of equipment powered by a range of energy sources. Modern applications such as industrial gas turbines and a great variety of ingenious farming equipment continue this great tradition. Indeed, the county still has a fully employed firm of millwrights.

That a president of the Newcomen Society, the national body for historical engineering, and writer of the authoritative "The English Traction Engine" should, in 1955, publish his researches into Lincolnshire's diverse engineering production is an indication of the importance of the county's contribution to the national scene.

The requirements of agriculture, the fishing industry, river boats, railways and two world wars have all been catered for by Lincolnshire engineers. Some businesses remained small supplying a specific need; others became of world-wide significance.

The book contrasts the entrepreneurial talents of the local blacksmiths and ironfounders with the later concentration of large-scale production in five Lincolnshire towns. From lift pump to showman's engine; steam hoist to steam navvy; beam engine to road roller; steam locomotive to petrol powered car; boiler to winding engine; marine winch to semaphore signal; all are here in this compact pocket book.

Alas, few of the engineering companies listed still survive, and electrical power with its associated electronics and computerisation have replaced most of the machines Ronald Clark refers to. This book has been out of print for the lifetime of many who will purchase a copy of this reprint. No attempt has been made to re-write or modify the volume, it is important as it stands. However, any corrections will be welcomed, and if necessary a corrigenda will be compiled for inclusion in future editions. As Chairman of the Society for Lincolnshire History and Archaeology I warmly welcome this important book on Lincolnshire's engineers.

NEVILLE BIRCH

Chairman, SLHA, September 1998.

THE FIRMS

THE ILLUSTRATIONS

PREFACE

I TRUST the same kind reception will be extended to this, my last county book, as has been shown to the other two, *Steam-Engine Builders of Norfolk* and *Steam-Engine Builders of Suffolk, Essex and Cambridgeshire*. I feel this should be the last because I think any other counties should be dealt with by an author qualified by residence near or within them.

While it is true that some Lincolnshire engineering firms are probably better known in a general way than their opposite numbers in the counties of Norfolk, Suffolk, Essex and Cambridgeshire, there are others, little known, which have long since ceased to exist, and it has been my endeavour to record the efforts of all in steam-engine building so far as it is possible within the small compass of a book of this size. It has been kept to this size to conform with my two previous books in order that the enthusiast may have all three bound up together. To make the set as complete as possible, additions, corrections and indexes have been included to cover all three.

Once again I have to thank all those many friends who have helped me in various ways and some firms still in business who have borne patiently my many demands on their time, have loaned me photographs and blocks, extended to me hospitality and permitted me to burrow unhurriedly into their records and archives. In particular, my thanks are due to H. C. Casserley, Esq., of Berkhamstead, for permission to use his photograph in Figure 107, to T. G. Hunt, Esq., of Smethwick, for permission to use his illustration in Figure 33, and George Watkins, Esq., of Bristol, for permission to reproduce his prints in Figures 5, 116 and 128. I must also thank Messrs. Aveling-Barford Ltd., Messrs. Harper, Phillips & Co. Ltd., The Grantham Boiler & Crank Co. Ltd., Messrs. Marshall, Sons & Co. Ltd., Messrs. Robey & Co. Ltd., and Messrs. Ruston & Hornsby Ltd., who have loaned me illustrations and blocks.

From the bibliographical aspect I think the value of all three books has been enhanced by the use of firms' original and authentic catalogue and press blocks when available.

In searching for details of technological history for these and other works it has been brought home to me very forcibly how very quickly such information becomes lost and forgotten and relevant literature destroyed. I must emphasise that some of the facts in the following pages were obtained only just in time since the end of the second world war, for such is the shameful rate of destruction of literature and records relating to the steam engine in this fair land—the land of its origin. As I mention in the text, the illustration for Figure 3 was given me as salvage and had I not acquired the originals of Figures 15 and 16 they too would have been pulped. In one amusing encounter the ancient son of the original patentee of a certain engine illustrated was, at first, in a disinterested way, quite emphatic that he had nothing relating to his father's engines. However, after much diplomatic discussion a complete cata-logue was found in the bottom of an old tool-chest in his kitchen!

In another instance a certain firm—let us not enquire their name—was quite definite that no records were preserved of their steam engines. Somewhat reluctantly permission was given me to have a hunt in the only place where their records might be found. At first the official concerned was obviously amused as he left me to it but when, after two hours searching, I showed him the negatives of all the engines the firm ever made, his demeanour turned to apology and awe as he stammered, "Good lord, I never knew they were there"!

Again, in yet a third case, I was ushered in to a gentleman who shone with a virtue resplendent in city garb. Upon my asking for details of steam engines once made by his concern, he fixed me with lack-lustre eye and enquired, "Are you an antique dealer?" I replied, politely, in the negative. Later, I met the principal with great success and learned all about their steam engines and also that the resplendent being was merely the accountant!

But why must England be so ashamed that she once led the world in steam-engine building? It therefore behoves all those interested to record what data they can and to preserve all official literature—sometimes not valued even by the firm concerned—when they obtain it.

Most of the usual types of engine were made in Lincolnshire, as were some unusual examples, including the curious portable engine by Barrett of Horncastle, the Clayton and Hornsby Tram engines, Harper-Phillips form of rotary engine, Howden's portable of 1841, Taplin's traction engine and many of the Tuxford engines. In fact, as a maker, William Tuxford showed as much if not more diversity than any other maker of his period and some of his types have become practically classics. Two truly historic engines and the first two built in the county are William Howden's marine and portable engines of 1826 and 1839 respectively. It is a great pity that no illustration is known to me of his marine engine as it must have been of a very original design.

Regarding the preservation of actual prototype engines, the most effective way to preserve them, of course, is to let them remain in their original position where this is practicable, as the right "atmosphere" is retained, but where not so, the problem is indeed difficult. Self-moving and portable engines are easier as, being movable, they can be stored in any suitable yard or corner (even in a front garden in one case!) so long as they are suitably protected. Local museums are scarcely interested, and as they obviously prefer to continue their profound slumber, private enterprise is proving a successful alternative in many instances. But, all the same, there is needed a virile organisation—may I say on the lines of the National Trust?—sufficiently interested in all types of steam engines (and possibly historic oil engines), to tackle their preservation both seriously and practically. At the same time, the newly formed National Traction Engine Club, of 52 Bedford Row, London, w.c.1, is a step in the right direction and its members will no doubt be active in saving a number of traction and portable engines ere it is too late. It is also making itself responsible for the organisation of future Traction Engine Rallies whereby the ordinary public may be educated into appreciating just how useful these engines can be.

As the reader will see on a previous page, my forthcoming

The English Traction Engine is in process of being written, although I cannot promise it within a year. But my friends may rest assured that where their names and addresses are known they will be appraised of it at the appointed time. Such a book is naturally somewhat of a co-operative effort and if any reader has photographs or information which he feels might be helpful I should be pleased to be allowed to see them, and make due acknowledgments if used.

Lincolnshire possesses a charm denied those whose only knowledge of it may be the Great North Road or that between Lynn and Grantham. It is a charm which demands return visits from personalities who once come under its spell, and I am pleased to say the researches necessary to enable me to write this book have been the occasion of many happy return visits. They have taken me to many parts of this large and varied county, accounting for many hundreds of miles by motor-cycle, thereby enhancing the task and making the labour a pleasure.

RONALD H. CLARK

Diamond Cottage
Shotesham All Saints
Norwich

Steam-Engine Builders of Lincolnshire

❖ ❖

I. T. ATACK

Jamson Bridge Iron Works, Market Rasen.

Little appears to have been recorded about Thomas Atack except that he was well established in 1865, but the dates of his commencing and finishing in business are lacking. In an old advertisement he describes himself as "Millwright, Engineer, Iron & Brass Founder", and, in addition, he made portable and fixed steam engines and the necessary boilers, besides a varied selection of agricultural implements.

Unfortunately I have been unable to trace an illustration of any of his engines although it is known that several of his portable engines were sold and worked for many years in this part of the county.

II. AVELING-BARFORD LTD.

Invicta Works, Grantham.

The most recently established firm in the county resulting from the fusion in 1934 of two very famous firms, viz. Messrs. Aveling & Porter Ltd., of Rochester, Kent, and Messrs. Barford & Perkins Ltd., of Peterborough. Thomas Aveling, born at Elm, Cambridgeshire, on 11 September 1824 (his birthplace cottage is still existing), moved to Kent as a young man and founded a small agricultural engineering business in Rochester in 1850. The first traction engine made in his works appeared at the Leeds Show in 1861, and since then *Aveling* engines and rollers bearing the famous Rampant Horse of Kent and the motto *Invicta* (sometimes cast in Lombardic capitals) have become famous all over the world. He was joined in partnership by Richard T. Porter in 1862 when the growing concern became Aveling & Porter Ltd. Similarly Barford & Perkins had an interesting origin. A certain W. P. Stanley founded a small business in Peterborough in *c.* 1840 and was

FIGURE 1. Aveling-Barford latest steam roller

engaged in making castings and agricultural machinery, etc. Apparently he deceased *c.* 1860 when young William Barford (born 1832 and deceased 1898), in company with a friend named Amies, purchased the business as a going concern and called it Amies, Barford & Co. Their full accomplishments comprised "General Ironmongers, Iron Merchants, Iron Founders, Machinists & Agricultural Implement Makers", and their address was Market Place & Queen Street, Peterborough. Upon Amies dropping out or dying, Mr. Thomas Perkins came in, for by 1879 it was Barford & Perkins, and, later, Barford & Perkins Ltd., and as such it remained until 1934. By 1904 Barford & Perkins Ltd. had produced the first of their motor rollers, which were to become, like Aveling & Porter's steam rollers, world famous. Incidentally, both establishments joined the Agricultural & General Engineers Ltd. in 1920. The fusion of the two concerns, both specialists in the two forms of road- and path-rollers, resulted in the best features of each type being retained and developed at Grantham.

In the steam-roller section the range was narrowed to five sizes, three having single cylinders and two double-crank compound cylinders, the weights in working order of each being respectively 6.6, 8.55, 10.5, 8.75 and 10.75 tons. A typical present-day Aveling-Barford steam roller is reproduced in Figure 1, which illustrates their type T single-cylinder machine. All in the range work at 200 P.S.I., have piston valves operated by Stephenson link motion, and both front and rear rolls are water ballasted as specified in William Barford's Patent of 1862. Very many modern requirements are embodied in these engines including constant mesh change speed gearing, total enclosure of steering worm and gear, crosshead-driven feed pump and, in particular, a stayless type firebox requiring no roof stays. A differential is incorporated in the transmission, and access to the tender and manstand is from the rear, with a coal bunker on either side—an idea first applied to some of the early traction engines.

These excellent steam engines are made as and when required and are one of very few makes still on the English market.

III. A. Y. BARRETT & CO.
Union Foundry, Foundry Street, Horncastle.

A. Y. Barrett established his small jobbing foundry, which gave its name to the street concerned, shortly after 1842, having taken over the business of Thomas Tupholme, "Brazier & Tinplate Worker", which was accredited in the town (in High Street) as early as 1835. By 1849 the firm was styled A. Y. Barrett & Co., "Engineers, Iron & Brass Founders, manufacturers of agricultural implements", but nothing more was heard of them after 1855, although it is reputed that about this time Mr. Barrett left the district, and became associated with Messrs. Barrett, Exall & Andrews, steam-engine builders in Reading.

Mr. Barrett's most famous engine is his portable of 1848, depicted in the diagram in Figure 2, from which it will be seen that the cylinder is mounted on a species of bedplate in turn

3

FIGURE 2. Unusual portable engine by Barrett of Horncastle

riveted on the boiler shell—an idea reverted to by many makers in this century. The bedplate is in effect a comprehensive saddle serving also as a base for the crankshaft-bearing brackets. The unique feature is to be found in the piston rod, which is bowed with the connecting rod contained within driving back on to the crankpin, the tail end of the piston rod being located in a gland through the chimney. The centres of the short connecting rod were only 1 ft. 7 in., the piston stroke being 10 in. The boiler, dome and wheels, however, are typical of the period and district.

IV. BLACKSTONE & CO. LTD.
Rutland Ironworks, Stamford.

Founded by Henry Smith in 1837 with premises in the Sheep Market, it was first known as Henry Smith & Co. After five years, in 1842, the business had so expanded that a move was

4

made to larger premises in Rutland Terrace, the new works being known as the Rutland Terrace Ironworks. In 1853 Henry Smith was joined by T. W. Ashby, the title now becoming Smith & Ashby. Again the works expanded when further new premises were obtained in Tithe Yard, on the north side of St. Peter's Street. Mr. Smith retired in 1857, leaving Mr. Ashby to carry on the business alone under the new title T. W. Ashby & Co. Upon Mr. G. E. Jeffery joining Mr. Ashby in 1868 the firm was now styled Ashby & Jeffery, and when in 1870 Mr. Luke joined them, the full title became Ashby, Jeffery & Luke. Six years later, in 1876, Mr. Luke and Mr. Ashby retired, leaving Mr. Jeffery on his own for one year, after which (in 1877) he took into partnership a certain Mr. Edward Christopher Blackstone, to form Jeffery & Blackstone, their address being the Rutland Ironworks. Now although Mr. Jeffery sold out his interest in 1882 the firm continued as Jeffery & Blackstone until 1889, when Mr. Blackstone turned it into a limited liability company to make Blackstone & Co. Ltd., as it is known today. A move was made to new works in 1887 (erected the previous year) on a site adjacent to the G.N.R. line from Essendine to Stamford, which still forms, with some recent additions, the present works.

As Smith & Ashby they were engaged in making all kinds of agricultural machinery, but by c. 1865 they had commenced the manufacture of portable engines, and a good representative example of the class is seen in the old print reproduced in Figure 3, salved in the nick of time from an isolated cottage in a Cambridgeshire Fen. The boiler has the firegrate in front and the single flue returns above, the smoke escaping via the very tall chimney mounted over the front end. The cylinder is mounted on the side of the boiler and also at the front end, and has the slide valve in a small chest over it. A forked connecting rod connects to the crankshaft fixed at the back end of and across the boiler, with the flywheel of five spokes on the opposite side. On top of the boiler is the small c.i. fluted steam dome mounting the throttle and Salter safety valves, the former controlled by a heavy Watt-type governor. They were very successful engines and quite a number were sold, although it is doubtful if one exists at the present time.

5

FIGURE 3. Curious portable engine by Smith & Ashby

FIGURE 4. *Left:*
Jeffery & Blackstone's
Viator engine

FIGURE 5. *Right:*
Winding engine by
Ashby, Jeffery & Luke

Another form of portable engine called *The Viator* was exhibited at the Newcastle Show in 1887, and consisted of a vertical boiler mounting a single-cylinder vertical engine on one side, the crankshaft being above and near the top as seen in Figure 4. The whole unit was erected on a wrought-iron frame supported on road wheels to make it portable. The boiler contained vertical tubes and the engine had a cylinder 5¾ in. by 9 in., and was controlled by a heavy centrifugal governor at 160 R.P.M. The list price was £100 complete.

Portable and semi-portable engines of orthodox layout were also made in fair numbers, utilising either single or duplex cylinders. A good example of the latter form adapted as a winding engine is depicted in Figure 5. Reversing was by means of Stephenson's gear with the nest of four eccentrics mounted between the cranks, the common valve chest being placed between the cylinders. The crankshaft bearings and the cylinder block were strongly strutted together by the circular ties seen in the illustration.

A few traction engines were made at one time and in 1871 one was exhibited at the Smithfield Show. It is a pity that no illustration has come to light to show its general outline, and apparently no contemporary detailed description exists.

In 1896 Mr. Blackstone commenced manufacture of the *Reliance* oil engine previously made by Carter Brothers of

Billinghurst, after which the firm gave up the manufacture of steam engines and concentrated entirely upon oil engines, the *Blackstone* oil engine now being famous the world over.

V. T. BRADBURY
Bridge Street, Gainsborough.

Thomas Bradbury carried on business as early as 1849 as a "Shipsmith" in small premises in Bridge Street. In 1855 he was classified as a "Blacksmith", but had reverted to his former trade by 1868. The firm probably closed down between 1890 and 1900.

During their existence they made several small vertical, horizontal and marine engines, and also a medium-sized beam engine having a single cylinder about 18 in. by 42 in., which was erected in Heckdyke Pumping Station on the west side of the Trent to drive a scoop wheel. This was the second beam engine installed here and replaced an earlier one erected in 1828. This second beam engine was in turn destroyed in 1933 when an oil engine was substituted.

Unfortunately no illustrations have been discovered to show the principal features of their various types.

VI. JOHN CABORN
Denton.

First mention of John Caborn is to be found in 1849, when he described himself as "Wheelwright & agricultural implement maker". In 1876 the business was in the hands of his son, Richard Spreckley Caborn, "agricultural implement maker & agent", but little more is heard of him after this date.

John Caborn exhibited, at the Great Exhibition in 1851, a portable engine of 7 N.H.P., which was equipped with governors and a "tubular boiler". Little information is available as to whether this boiler was of the return tube or multitubular form, and no record exists as to how many were sold, nor, unfortunately, has an illustration been found to show more details of its construction.

It is just possible that the boilers may have been bought ready made from one of the few firms in the county making them at this early period, and on such a boiler he erected and mounted the rest of the engine made in his own shop.

A later engine was rated at the unusual figure of 9 N.H.P., and had a much larger boiler than the first type. A trial returned the favourable consumption of 12.48 pounds of coal per H.P. per hour.

VII. CLAYTON & SHUTTLEWORTH LTD.
Stamp End Works, Lincoln.

A famous organisation established in 1842 as Clayton, Shuttleworth & Co., by Joseph Shuttleworth and Nathaniel Clayton. In the early 1900's they became Clayton, Shuttleworth & Co. Ltd., and finally Clayton & Shuttleworth Ltd. In 1929 they were absorbed into Marshall, Sons & Co. Ltd. (see No. XX). The engineering side of the business had been acquired by Babcock & Wilcox Ltd., when in Lincoln in 1924. At first the works comprised 1½ acres of land near the river and at certain times of the year was half under water. In 1917, during the first world war, railway work was undertaken in a new works known as Abbey Works, so named from its proximity to the neighbouring ruins of Monks Abbey. This subsidiary offshoot was called Clayton Wagons Ltd. Joseph Shuttleworth, who died in 1883, married a sister of Clayton's. Clayton was the son of Nicholas Clayton, a Presbyterian minister of Boston. In 1852 only eighty men were employed, but by 1906 the total exceeded 2000. The firm's engines were not numbered in numerical sequence until 1849. These portable engines had an exceedingly good market and the following table shows how the sales increased:

Year	Number of portable engines sold
1845	1
1846	2
1847	8
1851	126
1852	209
1863	395
1869	exceeded 1800

FIGURE 6. The Clayton first orthodox portable engine

At the commencement they were concerned mainly with cast-iron work and during this time Mr. Clayton was captain of one of the steam-boats on the River Witham, and in this connection he often visited the works of William Howden at Boston (see No. XIX). Howden had built, in 1839, what was probably the first portable engine complete, and here it was seen by Clayton, who produced his first and similar portable in 1845. It had duplex cylinders, 6 in. bore, placed horizontally on the double-flued boiler, and a wood frame ran along the sides and across the back supporting it. The crankshaft geared into a second shaft carrying the flywheel, the guide bars were round rods and the slide valves were operated by weighbars on top of the cylinders.

Their second portable engine had a boiler with a return tube at the firedoor end which went through the steam space in which was placed the chimney. The single cylinder was mounted on top of the boiler and the crankshaft was single ended.

Clayton, Shuttleworth & Co. claimed to be the first manufacturers to produce a portable engine having the now familiar and accepted layout, and a view of an engine of this class is seen in Figure 6, the first of the class having been made in October 1848. These orthodox Clayton engines had cylinders 6¼ in. by 12 in., 7 in. by 12 in. and 7¾ in. by 12 in. for the 4, 5 and 6 N.H.P. sizes respectively, the working pressure in each case being 45 P.S.I.

In 1853 appeared the interesting portable engine, seen in Figure 7, which carried off the first prize at the Gloucester

FIGURE 7. Prize engine by Clayton & Shuttleworth
at Gloucester, 1853

11

FIGURE 8. The 1860 traction engine and tender by
Clayton & Shuttleworth

Show that year. Its economy was due to the cylinder being
steam jacketed, the outside of the jacket in turn being heated
by the flue gases which at times would reach 400°F.

By 1860 the engine noticed in Figure 7 had been adapted to
the self-moving or traction engine seen in Figure 8, having a
single speed set of transmission gearing added and a fifth or
pilot wheel for preliminary steerage. The two-wheel tender
was detachable and when the engine was used for stationary
purposes it was used as the water cart.

Almost simultaneously the two partners produced their next
type of traction engine, included in Figure 9, and here chain
drive is preferred and the countershaft boasted a differential.

In 1876, at the Birmingham Show, appeared the all-geared
road engine depicted in Figure 10, with extra wide front wheels
for use in Fenland districts. Engines of this type could be
supplied with duplex cylinders if desired, and those of the
10 N.H.P. machine were $7\frac{1}{2}$ in. by 12 in. The specification was
very complete and comprised, among many items, a spring
footplate and also a brake; for the latter the makers claimed

FIGURE 9. Clayton & Shuttleworth's second type
of traction engine

FIGURE 10. All-geared traction engine by
Clayton & Shuttleworth

13

FIGURE 11. The Clayton Tram engine

FIGURE 12. A little-known Clayton product—their
horizontal engine

14

"it can be put into action instantly, and will be found of great use from holding the engine from running backwards".

In addition to road engines, the tram engine illustrated in Figure 11 was made in small numbers. This was basically a traction engine but with railway locomotive-type framing carried on two axles. Both axles were driven together by means of the endless pitch chain as shown.

A little-known *Clayton* product is the horizontal engine included in Figure 12 and a great number were sold since the first appeared and won a medal at the Great Exhibition of 1851. They were made in many powers ranging from 4 to 40 N.H.P., and could also be fitted with a jet condenser in tandem with the cylinder if the customer so desired. In 1890 the list price of the 40 N.H.P. machine with the tandem jet condenser was £420, which included foundation bolts, a third crankshaft extension bearing and a feed pump. The necessary Cornish or Lancashire boiler, also made in the works, was extra.

A vertical engine was also a standard product in the smaller powers and Figure 13 illustrates the range. They had a centrifugal automatic expansion regulator on the crankshaft which governed by adjusting the cut-off to suit the load, were of goodly proportions and, as can be seen from Figure 13, the finish was excellent.

By 1890 the firm's traction engine had been improved into the fine-looking machine depicted in Figure 14, having a large single cylinder, heavy duty gearing accommodating two speeds, and a hinged chimney. The last-named feature is somewhat unusual in a self-moving engine at this period and the crutch to receive the chimney is clearly seen in the picture. These engines were made in three sizes of 6, 8 and 10 N.H.P., and another feature stressed by the makers was "The Blow-off Cock is situated at the fore part of the firebox and can be opened without the attendant incurring risk of scalding".

One of the most interesting Clayton and Shuttleworth engines was their class of 0–4–0 shunting locomotive for standard and other gauges, and a photograph of *Pilot*, a typical example, is reproduced in Figure 15. In Figure 16 we have reproduced a sectional elevation and half plan from the original drawing. This type of engine had what were known as water tank

FIGURE 13. *Left:*
The vertical engine by
Clayton & Shuttleworth

FIGURE 14. *Right:*
Clayton's improved
traction engine

16

FIGURE 15. *Pilot*—the Clayton & Shuttleworth locomotive

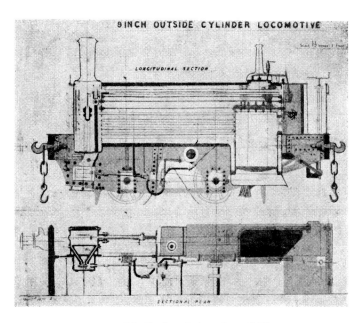

FIGURE 16. Sectional elevation of *Pilot*

frames, i.e. long water tanks were embodied on to the frames outside, and in this case were 14 ft. 7½ in. long inside, the cross section being 1 ft. 6 in. wide by 1 ft. 4 in. deep, giving a water capacity of 270 gallons. No dome was provided, steam being collected in a long perforated pipe extending in and almost the entire length of the steam space. Stephenson's link motion was fitted to each cylinder between the frames, the remaining details being easily discernible from the illustration. Other main particulars were:

Cylinders (2) outside	9 in. bore by 14 in. stroke.
Coupled wheels (4)	2 ft. 9 in. dia.
Wheelbase	5 ft.
Heating surface:	
Tubes (64 by 2¼ in. dia.)	276.88 sq. ft.
Firebox	32.93 sq. ft.
Total	309.81 sq. ft.
Grate area	6.22 sq. ft.
Coal bunker capacity	18 cu. ft.
W.P.	120 P.S.I.
Tractive effort at 85 per cent	4007 pounds
Overall length	18 ft. 11 in.
Overall width	7 ft. 6 in.
Overall height to chimney top	9 ft.

The drawing reproduced in Figure 16 is typical of the very high standard of draughtsmanship at this period, being beautifully drawn and tinted in water-colours to suit the respective materials. It was executed by Joseph J. Tyrrell, who was their chief draughtsman for many years and who, besides being an engineer of great standing, was a water-colour artist of no mean capabilities. This drawing is dated 1 May 1875, the locomotive being completed on the 22nd of the same month, and it bore the work's number 44701.

After the turn of the century the firm's traction engine was once again redesigned and altered into the impressive-looking machine depicted in Figure 17, here seen at the head of a typical agricultural train. They were made with single or compound cylinders, robust gearing and other parts, and a very full equipment of accessories. They were all four-shaft engines and were made in 5, 6 and 7 N.H.P. sizes, the last having a single

FIGURE 17. A later type Clayton & Shuttleworth traction engine

FIGURE 18. The redesigned portable by Clayton & Shuttleworth

cylinder $8\frac{1}{2}$ in. by 12 in., or, if compound cylinders, $6\frac{3}{4}$ in. and 11 in. by 12 in. A colonial type of traction engine was another product, but in this case the firebox was extra large to burn inferior fuels, and although only one road speed was provided, the power was transmitted to the road wheels through a friction clutch fitted to the inside rim of the flywheel.

At this period appeared their new design of portable, seen in Figure 18, which illustration is of that form, for service abroad, equipped for burning grass as fuel, which is automatically fed into the firebox by Head & Schemioth's mechanism. All the usual portable engine fittings are included and, as in the earlier engines, the range in single cylinders was from $2\frac{1}{2}$ to 14 N.H.P., and in compound cylinders from 8 to 30. A 40 N.H.P. size was supplied with duplex cylinders.

Very many overtype or semi-portable engines were made by Clayton & Shuttleworth in the early part of this century, and a good example is illustrated in Figure 19. They were very similar to the portable engines save for the road wheels and shafts, and the remaining details are easily studied from the illustration.

The advent of the Heavy Motor Car Orders of 1904 encouraged the development of the steam motor-tractor, and the Clayton example is included in Figure 20, which shows the compound machine, which was made with both single and compound cylinders. The highly efficient boilers worked at 200 P.S.I. Another special feature was the suspension of the rear axle on long laminated springs, thus eliminating most of the jar and vibration due to the shocking roads at this period. The compound cylinders were 5 in. and 8 in. by 9 in., and the single cylinder $6\frac{1}{2}$ in. by 8 in., using steam at 180 P.S.I. Several were supplied to the show business and one named *Oxford City* was a familiar sight in the south midland counties at one time.

Next came the most popular overtype Clayton steam wagon, included in Figure 21, of which hundreds were made in the Abbey Works. This embodied a small locomotive-type boiler pressed to 200 P.S.I., with the high speed engine mounted on top. The compound cylinders were 4 in. and $7\frac{1}{4}$ in. by 7 in. and, at a road speed of 12 M.P.H., developed 35 B.H.P. Trans-

FIGURE 19.
An overtype engine
by Claytons

FIGURE 20.
A 5-ton steam motor
tractor by Clayton &
Shuttleworth

21

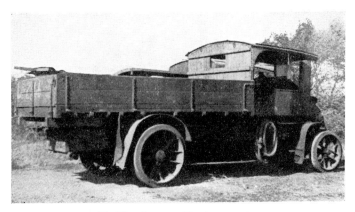

FIGURE 21. The famous Clayton overtype wagon

FIGURE 22. *Left:*
An erector's-eye view of
the wagon in Figure 21

FIGURE 23. *Right:*
A Clayton light-geared
railway locomotive

mission was by roller pitch chain, and two speeds were incorporated on the crank and second motion shafts. An erector's eye-view on the completed chassis is seen in Figure 22.

Following upon the orthodox overtype wagon came the undertype, where a vertical boiler was used containing a corrugated furnace with a special set of curved water tubes projecting into the path of the gases in a vertical plane. The undermounted engine had duplex cylinders 7 in. by 10 in., was totally enclosed, and both eccentrics were moved perpendicularly to the crankshaft by internally expanding and contracting folding wedges. With this simple arrangement the cut-off could be varied from zero to full gear instantaneously or progressively. With a vertical boiler and an undermounted engine a steam wagon had a shorter wheelbase than when a locomotive, and therefore a longer type of boiler had to be accommodated. Both types of wagon were shod with two 850 mm. by 160 mm. solid rubber tyres to each rear wheel and one 720 mm. by 160 mm. similar tyre to each front wheel. Besides making steam road vehicles the Abbey Works manufactured a number of light-geared steam railway locomotives for various railways at home and abroad, and as these have been illustrated and described profusely in the railway technical Press, it will suffice if mention be made of a representative engine, an outline drawing of which is appended in Figure 23.

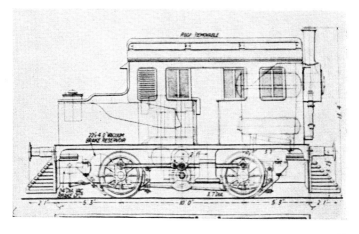

It shows one of two similar engines supplied to the Indian State Railways in 1930. The engines were of the four-cylinder vertical type grouped in pairs, each cylinder being 7 in. by 10 in., taking steam at 300 P.S.I. from a White-Forster boiler. Briefly, each boiler consists of a top drum and two smaller lower drums arranged like an inverted V, with two banks of curved tubes between them, the grate being below. The flue gases pass upwards through the tubes and then at right angles beneath the top drum and into the overhung smokebox and chimney seen in Figure 23. Such boilers were quick steamers and suitable for the high pressures involved. One engine was geared suitably for goods and the other for passenger service, the economical speeds in each case being 20 and 45 M.P.H. respectively.

VIII. COLLITT & CO.
Boston & Skirbeck Ironworks, Boston.

In 1887 Collitt & Co. took over the goodwill and premises of the famous Tuxford & Sons (see No. XXIX). Apparently they existed for only a few years as nothing more is heard of them after *c.* 1895.

Very little was manufactured in the way of steam plant by Collitt & Co., although they were responsible for the interesting agricultural unit reproduced in Figure 24. It is a steam baling press and was of the type exhibited at the Newcastle Show in 1887. The press itself, made under Harris & Rylett's Patent, is of well-seasoned timber construction. One side of the baling box is arranged to be taken out for abstraction of the finished bale. The pressure screws are operated by under-mounted sets of bevel gears driven off the end of the crankshaft of the small vertical single cylinder engine as shown. The salient feature of the patent (No. 13895 of 1887) was that by means of the long-pressure screws the compression plate could be made to move both upwards and downwards. Mr. Henry Harris was a hay merchant of 21 Trinity Street, Boston, but nothing appears to be known about Rylett, his partner. The engine is of the high speed open type and together with its vertical boiler is mounted on the end of a four-wheel truck, also of timber construction, with a swivelling front axle to facilitate move-

FIGURE 24. The combined engine and baling press by Collitt & Co.

ment from farm to farm. The finish was in "implement red" and the reader, upon seeing bales of straw in the fields today, can reflect that the power baling press is no new innovation!

IX. J. B. EDLINGTON & CO. LTD.
Phoenix Iron Works, Gainsborough.
A small firm established in 1868 by John Butler Edlington, who took Thomas Edlington into partnership to form J. B. & T. Edlington, classified in 1876 as "Engineers & Millwrights". In 1905 the firm became J. B. & T. Edlington & Co. Ltd., with premises in what was a small mill behind Lea Road schools. The present title is as above and they have a small branch works, the Victoria Iron Works in Brigg.
Only a few steam engines were made and they were all of the vertical type of a standard and straightforward design, but

unfortunately the present works are unable to find brief particulars or an illustration.

X. G. ELSTON
The Street, Welby.

George Elston, born in 1857 and died June 1931, became a threshing contractor on his own account and in his spare time built several steam engines between the years 1890–1900.

His first engine was a small portable of about $\frac{1}{4}$ H.P., having a single cylinder $2\frac{1}{8}$ in. by $3\frac{1}{2}$ in. using steam at 60 P.S.I., and a view of one of them is seen in Figure 25. The overall length of the complete engine is 3 ft., the overall width being 1 ft. 10 in., and the boiler contains seven tubes by $1\frac{3}{16}$ in. O/Dia. Altogether six portables of this size were made, the first five being sold to various showmen for driving small organs or for driving the pump supplying the water jets supporting the celluloid balls at shooting galleries, and the last was retained by George Elston himself for driving the lathe in his own small shop.

It was on this lathe that his seventh engine was made, a small traction engine this time, and a prospect of it is depicted in Figure 26. It is probably one of the smallest road engines ever made, the single cylinder being only $4\frac{3}{4}$ in. by $6\frac{1}{2}$ in., taking steam at 150 P.S.I., the overall length of the engine being only 10 ft. 8 in. Small though it is, its manufacture was a creditable piece of work in a small village shop, and the two engines illustrated are both existing in private possession and are used when required.

XI. FARMER, ROBEY, CLARK & CO. LTD.
Trent Foundry, Gainsborough.

A small firm commenced by Thomas Ardwick Farmer in small premises near the Market Place, just prior to 1842, when he was described as "Iron & Brass Founder", and continued so until joined by a son to form Farmer & Son by 1868. By *c.* 1880 the title was Farmer, Robey, Brown & Co., but shortly after 1884 Brown had dropped out, and by 1889 Clark had joined up with the former partners to form Farmer, Robey, Clark & Co. Ltd. The exact date when they finally finished business is at present not known.

FIGURE 25. G. Elston's little portable engine

FIGURE 26. A small traction engine also by G. Elston

For many years agricultural implements and ferrous and non-ferrous castings formed most of the firm's business, but in the late 70's portable and small vertical and horizontal engines appeared on the market. No illustrations have come to light to show the usual details of these engines although a small 2 N.H.P. vertical engine exhibited in 1884 had the generous cylinder capacity of 5 in. by 8 in. where the trunk guide was bored in line with the cylinder at one setting. Probably such a low rating with these cylinder dimensions was given to allow for very low pressures being used and at the same time giving the output specified.

A range of portable engines was also available and of these the contemporary technical Press said ". . . all of which are of good and recent design and well made and finished".

XII. WILLIAM FOSTER & CO. LTD.
Wellington Foundry, Lincoln.

A firm known all over the world and which was established in 1856 on a site on the Waterside North adjacent to Thorne Bridge called Wellington Foundry. In 1899 the works was moved to its present site and still called Wellington Foundry. At first the title was William Foster, "Engineer", but on 27 February 1877 Letters of Incorporation as a Limited Liability Company were obtained and the first Board Meeting of William Foster & Co. Ltd. took place on 18 June 1877. William Foster, the founder, was a miller by trade, so it is not surprising to find his first efforts were to produce grinding mills and all sorts of farm and agricultural machinery. Later he became well known as an agricultural engineer. He was Mayor of Lincoln in 1876. During the first world war Fosters did much development work in tanks and it was mainly due to their efforts in this direction that the later British tanks were so successful. Ever afterwards the firm showed a small replica of a tank as their trade-mark.

In 1863 William Foster advertised as a maker of portable engines, the first having been exhibited in 1858 at the North-allerton Show, where it won special commendation. Figure 27 illustrates a slightly later type duplex portable having Stephenson link motion and twin Salter safety valves, and very many

FIGURE 27. Foster's first design of portable engine

of these were made for both the home and export trade. It could be supplied without wheels if required in either the over- or under-type forms. The Foster portable was a very popular machine.

A special portable engine for the Colonies is seen in Figure 28, where the whole of the lower part of the boiler is encased and mounted on four small road wheels. The engine is really one of the firm's standard horizontals, having a planed base to mate up with a planed C.I. saddle permanently fitted to the boiler barrel. Note also the separate steam drum. They were made in from 3 to 10 N.H.P. sizes and worked at 60 P.S.I.

Figure 29 shows a large cross-coupled mill engine having duplex cylinders, high speed centrifugal governor, disc cranks, and a massive flywheel to ensure steady running and grooved for the necessary ropes comprising the drive. They were simple in design, used steam at 80 P.S.I., were made in from 12 to 50 N.H.P. sizes and would run for long periods without giving trouble. Several were supplied to power stations to drive large D.C. generators in the latter part of the last century.

29

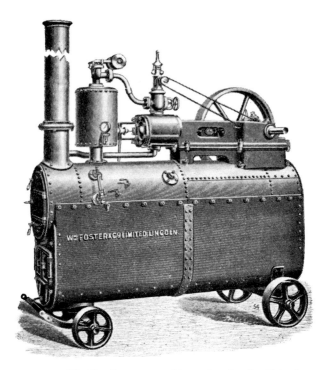

FIGURE 28. The Foster portable engine for the Colonies

FIGURE 29. A cross-coupled mill engine by Fosters

FIGURE 30. Foster's handsome little vertical engine

Their horizontal was made also in other forms comprising duplex cylinders arranged side by side and cantilevered over the end of the bedplate, bent crank and a governor-controlled throttle valve; or a single cylinder, four-bar crosshead guides and six-spoked flywheel, all on a rigid c.i. base and mounted on brickwork. Seven sizes ranging from 12 to 35 N.H.P. formed the range of these handy engines, the corresponding cylinder sizes being 11 in. by 22 in. and 19 in. by 36 in. respectively.

A handsome little vertical engine seen in Figure 30 was another stock line and enjoyed a range of from 1½ to 14 N.H.P. The 1½ N.H.P. had a cylinder only 4 in. by 7 in. and the 14 N.H.P. a cylinder 12¾ in. by 16 in. and ran at 200 and 110 R.P.M. respectively. Of these engines the makers said "The cylinder is carefully protected from contact with the air so that there is less loss of power from condensation".

Another modification of the vertical engine was the useful

FIGURE 31. A useful type of winding engine by Fosters

winding engine seen in Figure 31, where the complete unit—
engine, boiler, and winding drum—were all mounted on the
same girder frame truck on four road wheels for portability.
The vertical boiler was located in the centre and supported the
engine which drives the winding drum by a pitch chain through
a friction clutch controlled by a foot-brake. The engine was
quickly reversible and the drum was constructed with a thick-
ening casing, easily fixed or removed, and two working diam-

eters were quickly available to suit changing conditions of load and winding speed. Additional change speed gears could be erected on the crankshaft to provide still further speed variations. These winding engines were made in two sizes utilising the $2\frac{1}{2}$ and 4 N.H.P. engines having cylinders $5\frac{1}{2}$ in. by 9 in. and 7 in. by 10 in., lifting 20 and 25 cwt. on the smaller drum diameters and 7 and $9\frac{3}{4}$ cwt. on the larger drum diameters respectively.

With all these engines suitable locomotive, vertical, Cornish or Lancashire boilers could be made and supplied if the customer desired.

In later years W. Foster & Co. Ltd. have become renowned for their traction engines and road locomotives, and in Figure 32 we have one of their famous 7 N.H.P. general purpose traction engines, known as a Class ST engine, and utilising four

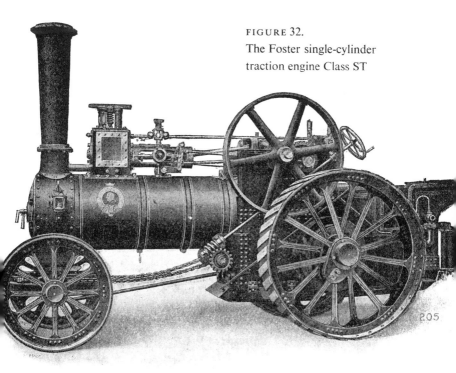

FIGURE 32.
The Foster single-cylinder traction engine Class ST

shafts in the transmission although the smaller engines use only three shafts.

Many fine road locomotives were made for travelling showmen, and in Figure 33 is seen a typical example complete with all fittings beloved of the showman. The 8 N.H.P. showman's engine had compound cylinders $7\frac{1}{4}$ in. and $11\frac{1}{4}$ in. by 12 in.

Like many other steam-engine makers this firm designed and made a 5-ton steam motor-tractor to comply with the Heavy Motor Car Orders of 1904 and appropriately enough called the *Wellington Tractor*. They have compound cylinders $4\frac{1}{2}$ in. and $6\frac{3}{4}$ in. by 9 in., and one of them in full working order is included in Figure 34. This example is yet doing useful work in the county of its origin. One attractive feature of the *Wellington Tractor* was the springing of the rear axle, covered by Patents Nos. 4151 of 1909 and 3010 of 1911. A semi-elliptic spring is used each side of the engine and is placed outside the horn-plate, and the variation in deflection, i.e. in spring length, is allowed for by permitting the ends of the spring to slide on a cam slipper-plate.

On several occasions Fosters fitted various self-moving road engines with Diplock's patent wheel or Pedrail, but perhaps the most interesting "special" ever turned out from the Wellington Foundry was a joint effort between W. Foster & Co. Ltd. and Richard Hornsby & Sons Ltd. (see No. XVIII), and a view of this most interesting engine is reproduced in Figure 35. The main engine, boiler and other major items were by Fosters while the tracks and transmission were by Hornsbys. The chain tracks were the culmination of a series of patents (suggested, no doubt, by the Diplock wheel in the first place) by Mr. David Roberts, of Hornsby's technical staff, and the engine, completed towards the end of 1909, underwent very extensive trials near Grantham in 1910. Mr. (later Sir) William Tritton (who afterwards did so much to perfect the tank), Managing Director of Fosters, was present at the trials.

Finally, there remains the Foster steam wagon depicted in Figure 36, embodying a two-crank compound engine with cylinders 4 in. by $6\frac{3}{4}$ in. by 7 in., mounted on a short locomotive boiler with Belpaire firebox, the working pressure being 200 P.S.I. Slide valves were fitted to each cylinder, operated by

34

FIGURE 33. A Showman's road locomotive by W. Foster & Co. Ltd.

FIGURE 34. Foster's Wellington tractor

35

FIGURE 35. The Foster-Hornsby Chain Track haulage engine

Stephenson's gear, and a double high pressure valve is included for ease in starting. Figure 36 shows the end-tipping body in action and also the single chain drive from the countershaft, the differential being incorporated in the rear sprocket.

It is interesting to note that Fosters made what may well prove to be the last traction engine to be made in this country. It bears the work's number 14738 and was delivered new in 1942 and is reputed to be still in service.

XIII. GREAT CENTRAL CO-OPERATIVE ENGINEERING & SHIP REPAIRING CO. LTD.

Fish Dock, Great Grimsby.

In 1889 they were well established as a company formed on a co-operative basis by several fishing-boat owners to further their own repairs, etc., and were entitled "Great Grimsby Co-op. Box & Fish Carrying Co. Ltd.", and their business was classified as "Coal Merchants, mast and block makers, and tinplate workers". By 1893 they had become reconstructed

FIGURE 36. Steam wagon by W. Foster & Co. Ltd.

under their initial title above and continued as such until well into the 1900's. Their new and last title necessitated their re-classification having more dignity as "Marine Engineers, Brass & Iron Founders". On account of their original title they were for many years, and sometimes are still, referred to colloquially as the "Box Company".

After 1893 they entered the steam engine trade and turned out a number of marine engines and steam winches. The marine engines included both compounds and triples and all were of the usual design of the period, having a piston valve to the high pressure cylinder in all engines, all valves being operated by Stephenson's link motion. They were usually fitted in drifters and trawlers and there may be several still in use.

The winches had duplex cylinders 6 in. by 11 in., with twin winding barrels and triple warping bollards each end of the barrel shaft. The cylinders had the slide valves on the inside in conformity with standard practice.

XIV. HARPER, PHILLIPS & CO. LTD.
Albion Foundry, Great Grimsby.

This firm was first established in 1870 by one George Drewery, a "blacksmith" in Queen Street, and in 1882 it was in the proprietorship of Alfred Drewery, whose address was 18 Albion Street. By 1892 the title had changed to Drewery & Harper, who were described as "Iron & Brass Founders", with their works in Eastgate. Drewery had dropped out by 1900 when it was Harper & Co. Ltd., classified as "Iron & Brass Founders & Makers of Mortar Mills", of the Albion Foundry, Eastgate. A year later they had styled themselves Phillips & Co., and by 1903 Harper, Phillips & Co. Ltd., as they are known today.

In the early 1900's Harper, Phillips & Co. Ltd., designed, patented and produced a most interesting steam engine, an external view of which is shown in Figure 37, whilst Figure 38 illustrates the interior with the outer cover removed. Briefly this engine consists of two moving slides, one moving inside the other and both being constrained in a square steam-tight box or cylinder. The inner slide A is really the crosshead and has the crankpin fixed to it at the far side (not shown) in such a

FIGURE 37. External view of Harper, Phillips
form of rotary engine

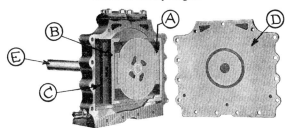

FIGURE 38. Interior view of the engine in Figure 37

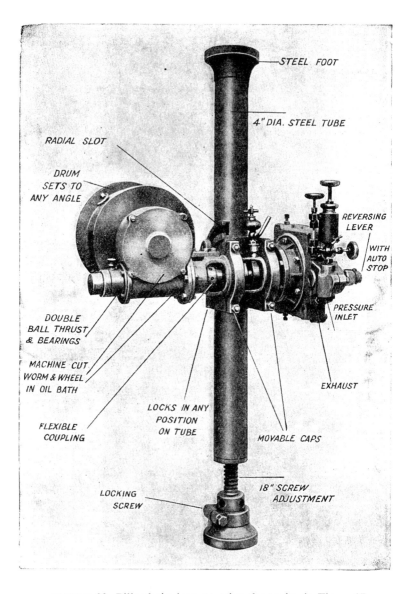

STEEL FOOT

4" DIA. STEEL TUBE

RADIAL SLOT

DRUM
SETS TO
ANY ANGLE

REVERSING
LEVER

WITH
AUTO
STOP

PRESSURE
INLET

DOUBLE
BALL THRUST
& BEARINGS

MACHINE CUT
WORM & WHEEL
IN OIL BATH

EXHAUST

LOCKS IN ANY
POSITION
ON TUBE

FLEXIBLE
COUPLING

MOVABLE CAPS

LOCKING
SCREW

18" SCREW
ADJUSTMENT

FIGURE 39. Pillar hoist incorporating the engine in Figure 37

40

FIGURE 40. The Harper, Phillips steam Seine winch

way that as the crankpin rotates the slide A reciprocates
vertically as well as horizontally. The outer slide B or piston
reciprocates only horizontally under the action of the steam
acting on it at alternate ends. In Figure 38 it is at the end of the
right-hand stroke and the swept cylinder volume is represented
by the cavity C. The outer cover D and the crosshead slide A
contain the necessary four ports. E is the crankshaft. As seen
from the view in Figure 37 these engines are compact, simple
and reliable, and a goodly number were made and sold between 1900 and 1914, as their applications were innumerable.
Their range was from 1 to 30 B.H.P., running at 800 and 200
R.P.M. respectively.

One very appropriate application of this unusual form of
engine was to driving portable pillar hoists for mines, docks
and so on, and a view of the complete apparatus is shown in
Figure 39, the illustration being self-explanatory. The total
weight of the engine and hoist was only 2 cwt. and the 2 B.H.P.
engine was used running at 800 R.P.M. Reduction ratio of the
worm drive was 24 : 1, the winding drum 10 in. dia. by 7 in.
wide between cheeks, and all mounted on a supporting tube
4 in. dia. by 7 ft. long.

In 1921 the firm produced a steam seine winch depicted in
Figure 40, having duplex cylinders 4 in. by 6½ in. fitted with

41

FIGURE 41. Portable engine by James Hart & Son of Brigg

Stephenson's link motion. The valve chests were on the outside for accessibility, but one great drawback was that they were not totally enclosed, and not a very great number were made.

Since then they have ceased to manufacture steam plant and have concentrated on ship work and the casting of propellers.

XV. JAMES HART & SON
Ancholme Ironworks, Brigg.

A small rural concern flourishing in the 60's and early 70's having a branch works at Caistor, and who described themselves as millwrights, iron and brass founders and makers of "Semaphore Signals", finally ceasing business *c.* 1880, when the goodwill and precincts were acquired by Mr. C. L. Hett (see No. XVII).

Besides "Semaphore Signals" they were also makers of a few vertical and horizontal engines and a number of portables of straightforward design, one of which is depicted in Figure 41. It is interesting in having an overhung crank on the offside end of the crankshaft, ribbed but unlagged single cylinder and spoked flywheel, and two fireholes, the main function of the upper door being to admit extra air for (more or less) perfect combustion. The chimney was very tall, even for the period, all road wheels were of wood and two horse shafts provided.

XVI. HEMPSTED & CO.
Phoenix Works, Grantham.

In 1852 one Robert Hempsted commenced his business of making agricultural implements in small premises in "George Street under Gentry" in Grantham. He was well established by 1868 and by 1872 we find there were no less than four connected firms in the town, namely:

(1) Hempsted & Felton, "Engineers, Iron & Brass Founders & Agricultural Implement Manufacturers", Phoenix Foundry, Earlsfields.
(2) George Hempsted, "Crank Maker", Grantley Street.
(3) Nathaniel Hempsted, "Crank Manufacturer", also at Earlsfields and Grantley Street.
(4) Robert Hempsted, "Engineer" (of Hempsted & Felton) and "Insurance Agent".

Apparently these four—there can be little doubt that they were really somewhat of a family affair—ultimately amalgamated, for by 1876 the concerns had become Hempsted & Co. Ltd., with additional offices in Finkin Street. By 1882 the "Limited" had been dropped and the title was simply Hempsted & Co. About this time the surviving Hempsted must have

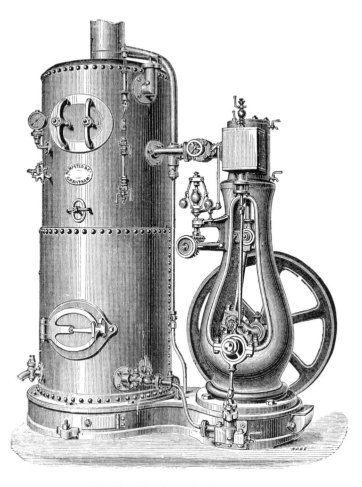

FIGURE 42. Glass Bottle engine by Hempsted & Co.

died, for in 1885 it was under the management of one William
Land, and was called the Grantham Crank & Iron Co. Ltd.,
and on 24 August 1905 acquired the title Grantham Boiler &
Crank Co. Ltd. as it is known today. The area now occupied
by the works and yards is $1\frac{1}{3}$ acres.

It was just prior to 1877 that the Hempsted family entered

FIGURE 43. The Hempsted portable engine

upon the manufacture of steam engines, and in that year they exhibited several engines at the Smithfield Show, their first type being represented in Figure 42. Their uncommon outline caused them to be dubbed "glass bottle engines"—a very apt description. Although open and accessible each side, the bottle-shaped standards acted as a guard against injury to the attendant and against oil-slinging. The details were of straightforward design and speed was regulated by a weight-loaded Watt-type governor. The feed pump was fixed to the common base serving the engine and vertical boiler. These "glass bottle engines" were made in three sizes of 3, 4 and 6 N.H.P.

Figure 43 illustrates their portable engine of this period. They had boilers of ample steaming capacity, two-bar crosshead guides, governor similar to that used on the glass bottle engines, and a large flywheel. This design was usually made in 7 and 8 N.H.P. sizes, although one or two charming little portable engines of 1½ and 2 N.H.P. were built and exported to France in 1883. Both had connecting rods 2 ft. 8 in. centres, crankshafts 2 in. dia., and a lock-up safety valve totally enclosed save for the hand-testing lever. The 1½ N.H.P. had

45

FIGURE 44. Later vertical engine by the
Grantham Crank & Iron Co. Ltd.

a cylinder 4¾ in. bore, the 2 N.H.P. a cylinder 5 in. bore and
both had a common stroke of 8 in.

Shortly after William Land assumed control the vertical
engines were redesigned in the form seen in Figure 44, where
the glass bottle effect is less pronounced and a high-speed
governor with its axis horizontal takes the place of the old
Watt type of instrument. Note that the slide bars and crankshaft plummer blocks are cast in the standards so that they

FIGURE 45. The Grantham portable engine and centrifugal pump

can never work out of line. Of these engines, the makers said, "Every part is accurately finished to template, and only the best materials and highest class workmanship are used throughout". The following table gives the sizes, cylinder dimensions and prices at the time:

N.H.P.	2 in.	2½ in.	3 in.	4 in.	5 in.	6 in.	8 in.	10 in.	12 in.
Cylinder: Bore	4½	5	5½	6¼	7	8	9	10	11
Cylinder: Stroke	7	7½	8	9	11	12	13	14	15
Price with Feed Pump		£24	£26	£28	£33	£40	£45	£60	£70	£88

In some cases the bedplate was made hollow to form a tank in which the boiler feed was preheated by a bleed from the exhaust steam. In the illustration the whole unit is shown mounted on four road wheels for portability. The firm made also a small centrifugal pump and in Figure 45 we have such a one belt driven off one of these small vertical engines taking steam from a standard vertical boiler, the lot mounted on a four-wheel road truck for use at fires and other emergencies

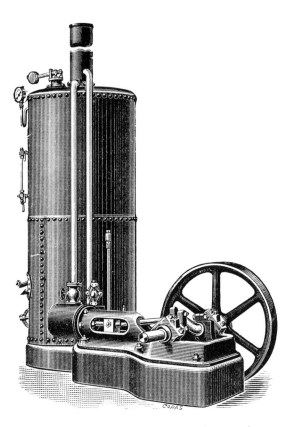

FIGURE 46. Horizontal engine by the Grantham
Crank & Iron Co. Ltd.

besides normal pumping duties, It is, of course, an early type
of trailer pump and it is therefore a sobering thought that the
idea of a light pumping unit capable of being towed behind
a vehicle does not emanate from the second world war!

There were, too, the horizontal engines, a typical example of
which is included in Figure 46. The general specification is
similar to that for the vertical engines except that the 2 and 2½
N.H.P. sizes were omitted. A few larger engines were made as
special orders, including a compound engine with cylinders
28 in. and 56 in. by 66 in., and a number of winding engines

48

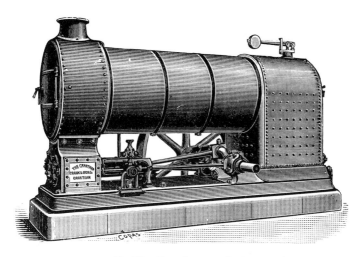

FIGURE 47. The Grantham undertype engine

having cylinders as much as 28 in. bore. The estimated date of these would be *c*. 1882 and no illustrations or drawings are now to be found, the only record being the bald entry in an old register of drawings.

Apparently the manufacture of portable engines ceased about this time, their place being taken by undertypes, a good example of which is illustrated in Figure 47. They were made in two forms, one having a single and the other duplex cylinders. Single cylinders were used in the 4, 5, 6, 8 and 10 N.H.P. machines and duplex cylinders in the 12, 14, 16 and 20 N.H.P. sizes. This class of engine was very popular at home and abroad at one time, occupying, as they do, less space than a horizontal engine and Cornish boiler of the same output.

After *c*. 1890 very few engines of any type were made by the firm as they went over almost entirely to the manufacture of high-class boilers and cranks of all types.

XVII. C. L. HETT
Ancholme Foundry, Brigg.

Charles Louis Hett was the eighth of thirteen children of John Hett and Louisa (née Nicholson) his wife, was born in

FIGURE 48. Charles Hett's vertical engine and centrifugal pump

1845 and deceased in 1911. He originally acquired the business, foundry and ancillary premises in *c*. 1880 from the then occupiers, James Hart & Son (see No. XV), upon their giving up business. Mr. Hett retired from active engineering in 1896. His private residence was in the Market Place and both the Hetts and Nicholsons were local Brigg families. The business premises were near to the local River Ancholme.

Charles Hett developed the hydraulic side of the former enterprise and very quickly had evolved high- and low-lift pumps driven by water-wheels and steam engines, all of his own make. The pumps comprised both reciprocating and centrifugal types, the latter being known as his *Accessible* on account of it being possible to dismantle the whole of one side by breaking only one joint. A typical pump is reproduced in Figure 48, illustrating it direct-coupled to one of his high-speed open-type steam engines. These engines had the valve chest on the side of the cylinder adjacent to the pump so that when used for marine work the engine could be placed quite close to a bulkhead. Steel was used wherever possible, and all bearing surfaces were of gunmetal. All moving joints were lubricated by self-acting lubricators which could be replenished while the engine was running, in this case at 500 R.P.M., the pump intake being 9 in. dia. This unit was made for and fitted in a steamer made and launched in Kingston-upon-Hull in 1886.

Other similar pumping units were made, one in particular having an *Accessible* pump direct-coupled to a smaller engine than that in Figure 48, which had the refinement of one of Morton's Injector condensers and was shown at the Amsterdam Exhibition in 1884.

XVIII. RICHARD HORNSBY & SONS LTD.
Spittlegate Ironworks, Grantham.

Richard Hornsby established his foundry in Spittlegate in 1815, and besides being classified as "Iron & Brass Founder" was, in addition, a "Paper Maker" in 1838. Eleven years later he was "Agricultural Implement Maker, Iron & Brass Founder, Paper maker". Richard Hornsby had three sons, Richard II, James and William, who by 1851 had joined their father to form Richard Hornsby & Sons, Richard the father dying in 1864. Of the son's children, only James William, son of James, entered the business, as did his two sons, Richard III and Capt. J. A. Hornsby, still living. In January 1880 the concern became a limited liability company and finally, in 1918, an amalgamation took place with Messrs. Ruston, Proctor & Co. Ltd. (see No. XXVI) of Lincoln to form Ruston & Hornsby Ltd. In 1940, Ruston & Hornsby Ltd. became associated with Davey,

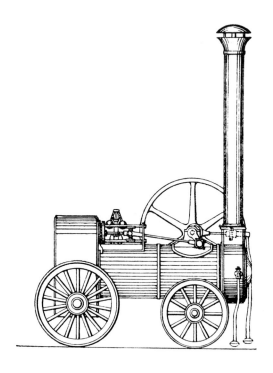

FIGURE 49. R. Hornsby's first design of portable engine

Paxman & Co. Ltd. of Colchester. Richard Hornsby and Sons Ltd. were one of the firms to whom Herbert Akroyd Stuart offered the manufacturing rights of his oil engines embodying his two great Patents No. 7146 of May 1890 and No. 15994 of October 1890, and in 1891 they agreed to undertake their manufacture. The firm also absorbed J. E. H. Andrews & Co. Ltd., oil engine makers, of Stockport, in 1906. In passing one may note that the Stuart patents, the former covering compression ignition and timed injection, and the latter covering the contracted neck to the vaporiser, anticipated by some little time the subsequent pronouncements of Dr. Rudolf Diesel. The compression ignition engine therefore is of English origin throughout.

Richard Hornsby produced his first portable engine in 1849, and a line drawing of one similar is given in Figure 49. Note that the cylinder is mounted in a steam chamber over the firebox, the top casing plates being carried up to contain it, and the crank is overhung on the offside. A feed pump is fixed to the chimney base and connected to a feed water heater mounted in the smokebox. These engines were made in four sizes of 4, 6, 7 and 8 N.H.P., the respective cylinder dimensions being $6\frac{1}{4}$ in. by 12 in., 7 in. by 13 in., $7\frac{3}{8}$ in. by 14 in. and $8\frac{5}{8}$ in. by 14 in. Note they were all long-stroke engines. In course of time a number of minor modifications were made and developed into the form of engine seen in Figure 50, the photograph being taken of an existing engine working in 1949.

In 1863 Hornsby made his first traction engine under Bonnall & Astbury patents and a line drawing showing the main details is to be seen in Figure 51. Note that railway locomotive influence is much in evidence, as witnessed by the cylinders

FIGURE 50. The Class D Hornsby portable engine

53

FIGURE 51. First traction engine of 1863 by Richard Hornsby

placed below the boiler barrel and close to the smokebox. Trunk crosshead guides were used and final drive was by chain from the countershaft to the rear axle. Beneath the engine and motion was the water tank, and the front axle was arranged to steer. Apparently very few of these engines were made although the design was very neat and possessed a number of original features.

Later, a traction engine of more orthodox layout was produced and exhibited at the Smithfield Show in 1880 and became one of the best known Hornsby products, some of them operating for their owners for very many years. Figure 52 shows a good representative example of the type, the photograph being taken of the engine (No. 6557) at work in Lincolnshire in 1946, it having left the works on 15 August 1889. All were made on the three-shaft system and of 5, 6, 8, 10 and 12 N.H.P. and worked at 120, later 140, P.S.I. The main points in the design were a differential, a crankshaft having the gear keys formed solid with it, a brake, and the belt for driving other machinery could be taken in either direction running quite clear. The makers described it as an "Improved Patent Narrow-Gauge Agricultural Locomotive or Traction Engine".

The portable engine continued to be in demand and an improved type known as the Class E was produced, one being illustrated in Figure 53. Note the heavily weighted governor

FIGURE 52. Hornsby's later traction engine

FIGURE 53. The Class E Hornsby portable engine

FIGURE 54. A Tram engine by R. Hornsby & Sons

actuating the expansion gear, therefore keeping the cut-off proportional to the load, the fine gib and cottered big-end and the duplex belt drive to the governor. The crankshaft brackets were adequately tied back to the firebox and other fittings included a whistle, spark catcher, Salter safety valve and bulb lubricator. The single-cylinder form was used for the 2½, 3, 4, 5, 6, 7, 8, 10 and 12 N.H.P. sizes but for the larger examples of 14, 16, 20, 25 and 30 N.H.P. duplex cylinders were employed. The customer also had an extra choice of duplex cylinders in the 8, 10 and 12 N.H.P. sizes if desired.

A little-known Hornsby engine is depicted in Figure 54, which illustrates their "Improved Tramway Locomotive" and which was an adaptation of their agricultural road locomotive to standard gauge of rails. The two-speed gear was retained, altered by a single lever, the gears being of crucible cast steel. With two speeds such engines could move a heavy load in low gear and save time on the empty return journey by using top gear. Four sizes were offered of 6, 8, 10 and 12 N.H.P.

Stationary engines were also turned out at Grantham and a representative view of their Class I compound horizontal engine is included in Figure 55. Note that they were erected on to a built-up base thus making them self-contained. The governing is by an automatic expansion regulator controlled by the powerful governor so that the cut-off in the high-pressure cylinder is always suited to the load, and so these engines became renowned for their economy. Steam was required at 140 P.S.I. The range comprised ten sizes from 6 to 50 N.H.P., the first having cylinders $4\frac{3}{4}$ in. and 8 in. by 10 in. and the last 14 in. and $22\frac{1}{2}$ in. by 24 in., the respective maximum indicated horse power for short periods being 20 and 160.

The engine depicted in the previous figure is arranged to take steam from a separate boiler, but where compactness was of prime importance it could be combined with a locomotive-type boiler to form an undertype compound engine, as seen in Figure 56, which also illustrates the inclusion of a surface condenser driven in tandem off the tail end of the high-pressure piston rod, the rest of the engine remaining very much the same. The makers claimed that by adding a condenser the I.H.P. was increased by $\frac{1}{8}$ to $\frac{1}{4}$ of the non-condensing horse-power figures.

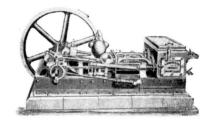

FIGURE 55.
Hornsby's horizontal engine known as Class I

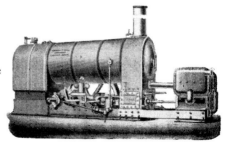

FIGURE 56.
The Hornsby undertype with tandem condenser

FIGURE 58. *Above:*
Hornsby's fine cross-coupled
geared winding engine

FIGURE 57. Vertical engine and boiler by Hornsbys

Figure 57 shows Richard Hornsby's vertical engine and
boiler designed for the export trade and therefore made as
simple and trouble-free as possible. The engine is erected on a
standard formed of the frustum of a cone and therefore very
strong. As the cylinder is fitted to the top of the cone by a deep
spigot the two parts must always be in perfect alignment. They
were intended only to fill a need for small powers and the range
comprised 1, 1½, 2, 2½ and 3 N.H.P. sizes, the cylinder of the
first being only 3 in. by 4½ in. and that of the last 5 in. by 7½ in.,
the corresponding speeds being 300 and 200 R.P.M.

Mining plant has formed one of this country's important
exports for many years and two types of horizontal winding
engines were made, one having direct-acting drive and the
other simple reduction gearing; a view of the former type is
seen in Figure 58. Both had cross-coupled duplex cylinders
lagged with polished strip mahogany or teak held by brass
bands, and the finish of these engines was of a very high order.
An exhaust steam feed water heater gave them great economy
in fuel and the loco-type boiler could be arranged to burn wood

58

FIGURE 59. A Hornsby portable engine with return-tube boiler

or other foreign inferior fuel. The range of direct-acting engines comprised 16, 20, 25 and 30 N.H.P. sizes, the 30 N.H.P. size being the largest engine made by the firm, having cylinders 12½ in. by 22 in., and a winding drum 4 feet diameter, which made 100 R.P.M. normal winding. At this rate the rope speed was 1250 F.P.M. and the load hauled one ton. The largest geared engine dealt with a load of 48 cwt. but at a reduced speed of 450 F.P.M.

The last type of steam engine designed was the unusual portable depicted in Figure 59, of which the engine portion was quite orthodox but where the boiler was of the return-tube form. The firebox was circular and the gases passed to the far end (dry-back) and returned to the front through a nest of ordinary tubes and thence up the chimney, which was at the same end as the firebox. Note that the smokebox is detachable by undoing the ring of bolts and, as the regulation and all firing was done at the same end, the other (flywheel) end was left clear for belt driving. They were made in the standard single-cylinder sizes and the finish was very fine.

After Messrs. Hornsby & Sons Ltd. had commenced the manufacture of oil engines in 1892 both types of prime mover were made for a time, but after 1906 the making of steam engines was discontinued although spare parts for some of the engines described were supplied for many years afterwards.

They co-operated, however, in the completion of the interesting special engine illustrated in Figure 35, the engine parts of which were made by W. Foster & Co. Ltd. (see No. XII), as we have seen.

XIX. WILLIAM HOWDEN & SON
Phoenix Foundry, Boston.

William Howden, who had been an apprentice in the works of the celebrated John Rennie, Senior, F.R.S., at Blackfriars, London, commenced business in 1803 in a small shop called Phoenix Foundry, close by the Grand Sluice in Boston. In 1826 he was styled plain "William Howden, Iron & Brass Founder", but later he was joined by his son, and the firm, in 1842, was called William Howden & Son. By 1849 William senior still continued his works at Phoenix Foundry, although William junior had seceded from his father and carried on a small business in Spain Lane. After 1860 nothing more is heard of either of them, although one Benjamin Howden was engaged in the show business in the town in 1875.

William senior's first excursion into engine building was a small marine job installed in the first of several small vessels plying on the River Witham at Boston. He had probably commenced construction of the engine some time in 1826 and the completed unit made a trial trip towards the end of 1827, whilst a longer voyage was made from Boston to Lincoln on 14 December of the same year. The boat was 24 feet long B.P., and the engine was rated at $2\frac{1}{4}$ H.P., but unfortunately no exact details of this most historic engine appear to be preserved.

At this time Mr. Nathaniel Clayton of Lincoln (see No. VII) was in charge of one of the vessels and in this connection often met Mr. Howden at the latter's works. It is said that Mr. Clayton copied the idea of his portable engine from one made by Howden in 1839 and which he saw when in the Phoenix Foundry.

FIGURE 60. William Howden's unusual portable engine of 1839

This interesting engine is depicted in Figure 60 and it will be seen that the whole unit was erected on a chassis of seasoned oak mounted on four road wheels, the front axle having a turn-table for steerage. The engine had a vertical cylinder $8\frac{1}{2}$ in. bore, was rated at 6 N.H.P. and had the crank overhead carried on two "A" trunnions. A marine type crosshead connected the piston rod to the side rod, from which the power was taken to the crank by the connecting rod. Note the similarity between this engine and the side rod portable by William Tuxford (see Figure 121), and it is said also of the last named that he, too, took the idea of his portable engine from Howden.

Howden exhibited this engine at the Lincolnshire Show at Wrangle in 1841, after which it was sold and for many years drove a scoop wheel pump in an adjacent fen. What happened to it eventually is not known, but it is on record that the several marine engines made and installed by Howden in the vessels which plied on the River Witham finished up in Isaac Watt Boulton's yard at Ashton-under-Lyne.

XX. MARSHALL, SONS & CO. LTD.
Britannia Ironworks, Gainsborough.

William Marshall, the founder, had in his early years been the St. Petersburg agent for William Fairbairn & Sons, the well-known millwrights and steam engineers of Manchester. Upon the small engineering business of William Garland & Son in Gainsborough (they were ironmongers and implement makers, although the date of their establishment is not known) coming on the market owing to the death of the proprietor in 1842, William Marshall purchased it. These small premises were called Back Street Foundry and on his contemporary business-card William Marshall states these facts, and additionally proclaimed himself as "Millwright & Engineer", and his complete trade embraced "Moulds of every description, Engines & Machinery, Palisades, Bean, Bark & Clay Mills, Land & Garden Rollers, Ship Winches &c." Now by 1848 the works were called Britannia Ironworks, but in 1856 1½ acres of new land had been purchased, upon which the first building of the new works was erected—a small shop about 100 ft. by 30 ft.—and it is interesting to note it is still incorporated in the present works. William Marshall's two sons, James and Henry, were taken into partnership in 1857 and 1861 respectively to make it Marshall, Sons & Co., and upon the decease of the founder in 1862 it became Marshall Sons & Co. Ltd. It remained as such until 1936, when it became Marshall, Sons & Co. (Successors) Ltd., reverting to its old and familiar title Marshall, Sons & Co. Ltd. in 1945. During the next year an association was entered into with John Fowler & Co. (Leeds) Ltd., Leeds, also world famous for their engines and implements. William Marshall came of an old Gainsborough family and at the time he commenced his engineering business in 1842 his brother Thomas Marshall was in business as a "Malster".

Portable and small vertical engines were the first prime-movers made in Britannia Works, and by 1867 the former type

FIGURE 61. Medal-winning portable engine by
William Marshall of Gainsborough

had been so perfected that one of them shown at the Paris
Universal Exhibition won a Gold Medal, and in 1881 a slightly
improved example won five Gold Medals at Melbourne. One
of these exhibition engines is seen in Figure 61. The smallest
size was rated at $1\frac{1}{2}$ N.H.P., as was the case with the smallest
made by several makers at this period, and the largest at 12
N.H.P., all having a single cylinder. With duplex cylinders the
range was from 7 to 35 N.H.P. inclusive.

The vertical engines of this period were of standard and
straightforward design and complete with feed pump and
governor mounted on one side of the cylinder, with the spindle
horizontal. Usually they were supplied with a vertical boiler,
the lot being mounted on a common bedplate. The smallest, of
$1\frac{1}{2}$ N.H.P., had a cylinder $4\frac{1}{2}$ in. by 8 in., and the largest, at

FIGURE 62. William Marshall's vertical engine

FIGURE 63. A neat horizontal engine by Marshall & Sons

12 N.H.P., a cylinder 12 in. by 16 in. Very many of these useful engines were made and sold both at home and all over the world, and a good example of the type is depicted in Figure 62. Another neat design of this period is the horizontal engine seen in Figure 63, of which the makers said, "We construct these engines from 10 to 35 H.P.". The cylinder is cantilevered over the end of the bedplate and is lagged with strip mahogany, and the finish was very high class. The 10 N.H.P. had a cylinder 10 in. by 20 in., the 35 N.H.P. one 19 in. by 36 in., and all could be used with steam from 60 to 80 P.S.I. Many examples of this type were made and large numbers were exported.

Steam winding engines made their appearance at this time (1885), the basis being the portable engine but with duplex cylinders driving through spur reduction gearing, the drum located on a separate spindle alongside the boiler. Alternatively, a small vertical engine of new design could be used, steamed by a vertical boiler and driving the drum by single reduction gearing, the whole being erected on a three-wheel truck for portability. A general view of such a set is to be seen in Figure 64.

Traction engines have been made by many English firms in many types, and the first Marshall traction engine was of exceptional interest; a view of it is reproduced in Figure 65. It was first produced in 1876 and was of the undermounted form, i.e. the engine and motion were placed below the boiler, all being erected on plate frames as a basis. Steerage was by twin chains operated by a slantshaft and hand wheel, the last named being just visible in the picture.

Apparently the undermounted traction engine had only a short life and by 1881 they had produced their "improved traction engine", an illustration of one of these original engines being depicted in Figure 66. They were offered in three sizes, viz. 6, 8 and 10 N.H.P., and all had the front axle set well back beneath the boiler barrel, four shafts in the transmission and with a very long boiler. The list prices in 1883 were £350, £400 and £460 respectively, but if Church's Patent Circular Slide Valve was fitted the extra cost was £10 per engine. Very many of these grand old engines were made and the author saw one derelict as recently as 1945.

FIGURE 64. Winding engine by Marshalls in 1885

FIGURE 65. The first Marshall traction engine

FIGURE 66. Marshall's improved traction engine

FIGURE 67. Semi-portable engine by Marshall, Sons & Co. Ltd.

Variations of the portable engine are the undertype and overtype, the latter often called a semi-portable, and in Figure 67 we have a fine example of the former, having double crank compound cylinders, tandem jet condenser and single eccentrics. There were ten different sizes ranging from 8 to 60 N.H.P., those up to 30 N.H.P. being fitted with Hartnell governors and above 30 N.H.P. with Proell governors.

Figure 68 depicts a typical Marshall overtype or semi-portable engine which at one time were made by the score. It embodies the maker's famous *Britannia* boiler pressed to 100 P.S.I., the advantages of which were the absence of stays between the shell and firebox and a long grate in line with the lower part of the furnace door. The barrel contained tubes arranged in the usual way, the firehole plate being pressed into shape at one heat. The cylinder is set well forward on the crown and bored crosshead guides were used.

Illustrated in Figure 69 is one of the most famous engines ever made by any manufacturer—the Marshall Class L. Sold not only to many satisfied users in the United Kingdom but in other and remote parts of the world, the Class L became so famous that a separate handbook, bound in dark blue, was at one time issued by the firm to those interested, and the author

FIGURE 68. Marshall's overtype engine

FIGURE 69. The world-renowned Marshall Class L engine

69

FIGURE 70. Compound tandem Marshall Class L engine
shown cross-coupled

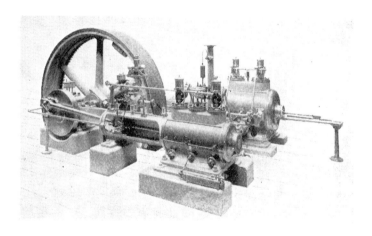

FIGURE 71. Compound Marshall Class L engine
when cross-coupled

has always regarded it as a miniature textbook on engine erection. These Class L machines were all long-stroke engines having jacketed cylinders and heavy flywheel, which, combined with the robust governor, ensured a speed variation of not more than 5 per cent from no load to a sudden application requiring a cut-off at 3/8 stroke. All had Marshall's Patent Trip Gear, comprising double beat drop valves to both inlet and exhaust, and layshaft operating gear driven by mitre wheels from the crankshaft. The cylinder sizes of Class L engines range from the smallest, 7 in. by 20 in., to the largest, 22 in. by 48 in., the latter having a flywheel 16 ft. diameter.

They were also supplied in tandem compound and cross-coupled compound forms, and a very beautiful example of the cross-coupled tandem compound layout is depicted in Figure 70, which set is rated at 1200 H.P. and is one of the largest steam engines built in the country. Each pair has cylinders 22 in. and 38 in. by 48 in. running at 75 R.P.M. Figure 71 shows the cross-coupled compound form, the low-pressure cylinder having a tailrod extension slide to take part of the weight of the large low-pressure piston. All the compound engines were made in a large range of sizes with cylinders varying from 7 in. and 13 in. by 20 in. to 22 in. and 38 in. by 48 in., and were suitable for working pressures from 100 to 140 P.S.I. The cross-coupled compound engines were known as the Class LC, the tandem compound as the Class LT and the cross-coupled tandem compound as the Class LHT. It is almost unnecessary to add that the finish of all these engines was of a very high standard indeed. They had a fine reputation because, as the makers said, ". . . great care has been exercised to cut down the clearance spaces to ensure the utmost economy in steam consumption".

In Figure 72 we have another famous Marshall compound engine, the vertical type Class MP, and here it is shown direct coupled to an ironclad generator, both engine and dynamo being mounted on the bedplate common to both. Speed regulation was maintained between extremely narrow limits by virtue of an inverted Pickering-type governor driven by a roller-pitch chain from the crankshaft. The reciprocating parts were partially enclosed, and these engines would run for long

FIGURE 72. Another famous Marshall engine—
the vertical Class MP

FIGURE 73. A Marshall duplex cross-coupled winding engine

FIGURE 74. The Marshall locomobile

periods without attention, their cylinder dimensions following closely those of the horizontal compounds.

In addition to the engine depicted in Figure 64, steam winding and hoisting engines had been developed to embrace duplex horizontal cylinders steamed by a loco-type boiler and spur-gear-driven drum, self-contained hoisting engines and drum all mounted on the same bedplate, and either compound or duplex cross-coupled engines driving the centre drum or drums by robust spur gearing. An engine of the last-named form is reproduced in Figure 73. The larger machines would hoist 70 cwts. at a rope speed of 1200 ft. per minute, the engine using steam at 100 P.S.I.

A very fine example of steam engine manufacture is to be seen in Figure 74, which represents the Marshall *Locomobile*; similar machines have been made for use not only in this country but places abroad as far apart as Australia, Japan, Greece and Holland. That shown in Figure 74 illustrates the crank end, the engine comprising double-crank compound cylinders fitted with piston valves, and the exhaust could be utilised for process work if desired. They were proved to be extremely economical in fuel consumption and the 250 N.H.P. size developed 313 I.H.P., with a coal consumption (12,500 B.T.U.s per pound) of only 1.09 pounds per I.H.P. per hour. Their boilers could be adapted to burn, besides coal, wood, sawdust, husks, shells and any other combustible trade waste. The construction of the boiler comprised a single corrugated flue forming the firebox, containing at the front end a tube plate carrying a number of ordinary smoke-tubes, and the whole unit—firebox and tubes—were withdrawable by undoing a series of nuts around the edge of the endplate containing the flue. The studs, of course, were fitted in the dished end. In this way the whole of the interior of the shell was made accessible for inspection and repair. The makers were justly proud of their economy and described them as "The most economical steam engines in the world".

The latest type of portable engine with the *Britannia* boiler (already described) is included in Figure 75, where speed is controlled by means of a Hartnell automatic expansion regulator, and an added refinement is the jet condenser eccentric operated off the end of the crankshaft. These engines —also mounted on an ordinary loco-type boiler—could be supplied in single cylinder, double-crank compound or duplex forms, and all worked at 150 P.S.I. The smallest in each range had cylinders $4\frac{3}{4}$ in. by 8 in., $7\frac{1}{2}$ in. and $11\frac{1}{2}$ in. by 12 in. and $6\frac{1}{2}$ in. by 12 in. respectively, the dimensions of the largest being $10\frac{1}{2}$ in. by 14 in., $9\frac{1}{2}$ in. and $14\frac{1}{2}$ in. by 12 in. and $8\frac{1}{2}$ in. by 12 in. respectively.

All the ordinary locomotive-type boilers were fitted with Marshall's Patent Anti-Incrustation firebox possessed of corrugations pressed in the crown and running from each corner, meeting in the middle, saltire fashion, which, as the makers said, "form an exceptionally strong truss to support the plate against the working pressure of the boiler".

Over many years the firm's traction engine had been developed and modified into the fine machine depicted in Figure 76, which illustrates the single-cylinder traction engine in its latest

FIGURE 75. A Marshall portable engine with Britannia boiler

FIGURE 76. The later type Marshall single-cylinder
traction engine

75

FIGURE 77. Marshall's compound four-shaft traction engine

FIGURE 78. Steam-roller Class S by Marshall, Sons & Co. Ltd.

form, having all the accepted fittings and equipment and, in particular, a rear grooved guide pulley and hand brake incorporated with the winding drum. They were made in four sizes of 5, 6, 7 and 8 N.H.P., the last named having a cylinder 9 in. by 12 in., and all of them used steam at 140 P.S.I.

Figure 77 shows the compound traction-engine used for heavy haulage, utilising four shafts in the train, and some were fitted with three speeds. They were very powerful machines and were in the same range of sizes as the single-cylinder type. The 8 N.H.P. compound would haul 14 tons up a gradient of 1 in 12. When used where there was a risk of fire, either at home or abroad, a spark catcher could be fitted at a slightly extra charge.

A natural modification of the traction engine is the steam-roller, and in Figure 78 we have the Marshall example as manufactured by them in India at the present time, with the exception of the boilers, which are made at Gainsborough. It is known as the Class S roller and could be supplied in from 6 to 16-ton sizes with compound cylinders and using the Marshall single eccentric radial valve gear. All wheels are of steel plate and the usual livery is a bright maroon lined out in yellow, and very handsome they look.

Our subjects also took up the manufacture of the tandem steam-roller in competition with several other makers, and the Millars-Marshall example is reproduced in Figure 79. It was a three-shaft machine and utilised a squat vertical boiler steaming a small horizontal engine with duplex cylinders, the engine being quickly reversible. This was effected by the application of Klug's single eccentric radial valve gear, which gave an almost instantaneous reversal, the valves being located above the cylinders. Steerage was from behind. The quick-reverse tandem roller was evolved to meet the demand for rolling hot asphalt and where a stoppage for any length of time at the end of a run would result in a depression in the surface—hence the necessity for rolling a narrow width and quick reversal.

After the Heavy Motor Car Orders of 1904 came the 5-ton steam motor tractor, and a view of one at work is depicted in Figure 80. They were built on the three-shaft principle and could be fitted with two or three speeds as desired and the usual

FIGURE 79. The Millar-Marshall tandem roller

FIGURE 80. 5-ton steam motor tractor by Marshall, Sons & Co. Ltd.

conventional fittings. The double-crank compound cylinders were $4\frac{3}{4}$ in. and 8 in. by 9 in. and normally a disc flywheel was used. Many of these handy little engines left Britannia Works and some are still to be found in use in unexpected places.

Finally, it is very gratifying to find that the Britannia Works

FIGURE 81. A Marshall Class K engine on test in 1950

are still turning out one type of steam engine (the other types are not now made), and in 1950 the author had the pleasure of seeing six in course of erection and a seventh on test; a picture of the last is shown in Figure 81. It is the present-day modification of the famous Class K engine, having a cylinder 13 in. by 24 in. developing a useful maximum load of 125 I.H.P. A piston valve is fitted, the cut-off being controlled by the governor through the expansion gear. Those produced so far are for use in tea plantations abroad and are some of the very few large steam engines being built in this country today.

XXI. HENRY B. MASSEY
Excelsior Engineering Works, Spalding.

A small engineering works founded by Henry Bateman Massey, F.R.A.S., in 1873. His premises were burnt out in a disastrous fire in 1893 but he restarted production the same year and deceased in 1907. He was succeeded by his son, William Burt Massey, who continued the firm until 1946, when it became absorbed into P. B. Bettinson & Co. Ltd., General Engineers, Holbeach, in the same county, and as such continues in existence today, Mr. W. B. Massey remaining a director.

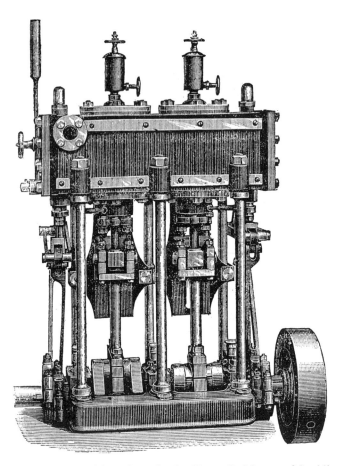

FIGURE 82. Small launch engine by Henry B. Massey of Spalding

Henry B. Massey, though well known for his light-type machine tools covering such items as shapers, planers, and in particular his ornamental turning lathes, was designer and manufacturer of a series of interesting little launch engines, and a typical example of the range is detailed in Figure 82. They all had duplex cylinders, the smallest being 2½ in. by 3 in., ". . . and is suitable for driving a boat about twenty-five feet long. The price is £30". A larger size had cylinders 5 in. by 5 in. and cost £55. The finish of all of them was of the very high order one associates with a machine-tool maker; all had Stephenson's link motion with quick-reverse hand-lever, and the cylinders were lagged with the usual polished strip mahogany and polished brass bands, the whole effect being most pleasing to the eye.

It is interesting to record that at one period the works, employing about thirty-eight men, was driven by a portable steam engine by William Tuxford & Sons of Boston (see No. XXIX).

XXII. E. MORLEY
Harlaxton Road, Grantham.

Established as Agnis & Yates in the '80s, this small concern later became Henry Yates, and after his death a relative, Thomas Yates, combined with Edward Morley to make it Yates & Morley for four years, until 1900, when Edward Morley became sole proprietor. He finally gave up business on 15 March 1932, when the little works in Harlaxton Road closed down, and the plant sold by auction, the premises now being used as a garage.

Much of the business was repair work to agricultural and similar machinery, including the re-erection of ploughing engines on new boilers, etc., but Edward Morley also made a number of small pumps for boiler feed and other purposes, and a general view of one is illustrated in Figure 83. They were of robust design and were made in three sizes, having a steam cylinder of $3\frac{1}{2}$ in., 5 in. or 8 in. bore. It is not recorded how many were turned out in the little works but there may be one or two of them existing and still at work in the Grantham district.

XXIII. PENISTAN & CO.
Broadgate Ironworks, Lincoln.

This small firm, established by Michael Penistan, acquired the premises formerly occupied by Watkinson & Robey (see No. XXV), and in 1863 proclaimed that they made an "Improved Portable Steam Engine", and an illustration of this workmanlike machine is seen in Figure 84. Its main features

G

FIGURE 83.
Boiler feed pump by
Morley of Grantham

include a regulator-cum-stop-valve inside the steam space above the firebox crown, large single cylinder lagged with mahogany, feed pump arranged so that resistance of its plunger is a maximum at half stroke of the piston, a Watt-type governor and the usual shaft for two horses.

They were made in five sizes, the cylinder bores and prices being as follow:

N.H.P.	Bore of Cylinder	Price
4	$6\frac{1}{2}$ in.	£150
5	7 in.	£165
6	$7\frac{3}{4}$ in.	£180
7	$8\frac{1}{2}$ in.	£200
8	9 in.	£220

FIGURE 84. Penistan's portable engine

No further mention of them appears after *c*. 1870 although it is on record that Michael Penistan, Robert Robey and Isaac Watt Boulton (of Boulton's Siding fame) would at times forgather at the Queen's Hotel, Lincoln, to fraternise.

XXIV. RICHARDSON & DARLEY
Lindsey Works, Kirton in Lindsey.

Little is known of this small firm who were well established by 1863 and who in that year advertised themselves as "General Engineers and makers of Improved Traction Engines etc".

It is recorded that they made one or two of these improved traction engines, but so far no details have been forthcoming to evidence what these improvements were, or illustrations to show what the completed engine—undoubtedly very interesting—looked like.

Nothing more is heard of them after 1868.

FIGURE 85. Robert Robey's first design of chain-drive
traction engine

FIGURE 86. Robey traction engine with Mackinder's
spring wheel

84

XXV. ROBEY & CO. LTD.

Globe Works, Lincoln.

A firm known all over the world as makers of steam engines and founded by Robert Robey in 1854, and whose address in 1861 was Robey & Co., Perseverance Works, Canwick Road. The next year he had turned the business into a limited liability company styled Robey & Co. Ltd., but by 1874 it had become Robey & Co., reverting to Robey & Co. Ltd. in 1893, as it has remained ever since. The present managing director, Mr. W. T. Bell, is a son of one of the original partners. It is interesting to note, however, that an earlier firm—Watkinson & Robey— were existing as early as 1849 with premises in St. Rumbert's Lane, but the present firm disown all connection with them.

It was in 1861 that Robert Robey advertised his first traction engine and at the Great Exhibition the following year the firm exhibited one of them having duplex cylinders, and rated at 10 N.H.P. It is represented in Figure 85. It had a stub counter-shaft beneath the manstand and both primary and secondary drives were by pitch chain. All road wheels were of timber construction (as used on other agricultural vehicles of their manufacture), steerage was arranged in front as shown, the crankshaft brackets were of best wrought iron and the chimney was hinged and had a crutch to receive it over the connecting rod. Another traction engine of this period had very large rear wheels fitted with a large internally toothed annulus into which meshed the single-gear driving-pinion on the offside end of the crankshaft. It bore the grand title of *Patent Highway Locomotive*. The cylinder was jacketed in the smokebox. A third layout used a similar configuration to that shown in Figure 85, but had a second shaft beneath the manstand mounting a large and a small sprocket. The first chain connected the crankshaft with the large sprocket and the second chain took the drive from the small sprocket to a much larger one mounted on the offside rear wheel. Neither of the two types last mentioned became very popular and they were soon dropped in favour of a more orthodox type of geared engine.

This geared road engine is depicted in Figure 86 and is fitted with William Mackinder's patent spring wheels on the rear axle. In this design of wheel the rim is fitted with a number of india-

FIGURE 87. A typical Robey portable engine

rubber pads or cushions, each being enclosed in a hollow steel shoe to receive it. These shoes are fixed to the rim by wrought-iron keys or stumps, allowing $\frac{7}{8}$ in. of radial play. Any shoe could be dismantled separately. The single cylinder and valve chest are mounted on the chimney end of the boiler and enclosed in a neat metal casing. The crankshaft is bent from the round bar made from the best hammered scrap iron and carries the pair of eccentrics near to the left-hand bearing.

A class of portable engines had been made from the earliest times of the firm's history and a good example of the type made towards the end of the last century is included in Figure 87. As will be seen the design was very simple and robust, with ample boiler capacity. The range comprised engines of from $2\frac{1}{2}$ to 12 N.H.P. with single and from 8 to 30 N.H.P. with duplex cylinders. The engine in Figure 87 could be equipped with Elworthy's apparatus for burning straw where the fuel is fed into the extra large firebox through a chute operated by one

FIGURE 88. The world-famous Thomson road steamer by Robeys

man. Very many of these engines were sold at home and abroad, with and without the Elworthy attachment.

The portable engine also served as a basis for their overtype, which, like their undertype engines, was made in all the usual sizes.

In Figure 88 we have one of the most famous historic engines ever made by the firm, to wit, a Thomson road steamer. Mr. Thomson, of Edinburgh, first conceived the design in 1867 when he applied vulcanised rubber tyres to the rims of road vehicles. Among several firms who undertook the manufacture of these engines for Mr. Thomson was Robey & Co. Ltd., and Figure 88 depicts their 1870 variety. The motive power was developed in vertical duplex cylinders $7\frac{3}{4}$ in. by 10 in., using steam at 100 P.S.I. from a vertical "Pot" or "Field" type of boiler. Two speeds were used in the gearing and the crank and countershafts were in constant mesh, the feed pump being driven off the latter. The driving wheels were shod with Mr.

FIGURE 89. A gem of a locomotive by Robey & Co.

Thomson's patent rubber tyres protected by steel tread plates, the front or steerage wheel being iron shod. Engines of this type were tested with loads of an omnibus containing forty-six passengers up the famous hill in Lincoln City at speeds of 4 to 5 M.P.H., a feat which they accomplished easily. Many readers will know this hill with its 1 in 9 gradient and therefore appreciate the performance.

In common with several other firms in the county at this time, Robey & Co. turned their attention to railway locomotives, and Figure 89 represents a little gem for 2-ft. gauge for use for industrial purposes at home and abroad. The two cylinders were at the front end, slightly inclined, and drove on to the back axle, the rest of the chief details being self-evident from the picture. A slightly larger version of the 0–4–0 wheel arrangement, named *Santiago*, is depicted in Figure 90. Here, side tanks take the place of well tanks as in the previous example, and one sand pipe enables sanding to be done in either direction. The finish was of a very high order and I leave it to the reader to picture the medium-warm green lined out with black

FIGURE 90. A larger locomotive also by Robeys

and white, the lot surmounted by the brass flared chimney and resplendent brass dome afforded the luxury of twin Salter safety valves.

Many forms of vertical engine have been made in the Globe Works comprising high speed single, compound and triple expansion, either open or enclosed. In Figure 91 is shown the standard single-cylinder engine and these were listed with a cylinder only $4\frac{1}{2}$ in. by 4 in. to one with a cylinder $14\frac{1}{2}$ in. by 14 in., the maximum speeds in each instance being 450 and 225 R.P.M. respectively. A typical compound engine and one most pleasing to the eye with its finely proportioned detail is shown in Figure 92. Of the open type, it is fitted with a jet condenser, piston valve to the high-pressure cylinder, and speed is controlled by Richardson's Patent Governor, the whole of the reciprocating masses being accurately balanced. They were made in seven sizes, the smallest having cylinders $11\frac{1}{4}$ in. and $19\frac{3}{4}$ in. by 12 in., and the largest cylinders 23 in. and 40 in. by 24 in. The triple expansion job is depicted in Figure 93 and there again the general finish, balancing and design are first

89

FIGURE 91. *Right:*
Robey's standard
single-cylinder
vertical engine

FIGURE 92. *Left:*
A Robey compound
engine most pleasing to
the eye

FIGURE 93. *Right:*
A triple-expansion
Robey vertical engine

class throughout. The shaft governor acted on the slide valve direct and maintained constant speed under all conditions of loading.

Horizontal engines of many forms were also stock lines and covered such layouts as single cylinder, duplex, cross-coupled compound, tandem compound and triple expansion cross-coupled. Most of these could be equipped with jet condensers in tandem behind the low-pressure cylinder, or, in the case of the last named, behind the high-pressure. Figure 94 shows the long-stroke single-cylinder horizontal Class E complete with jet condenser in tandem and auto-trip expansion gear with drop

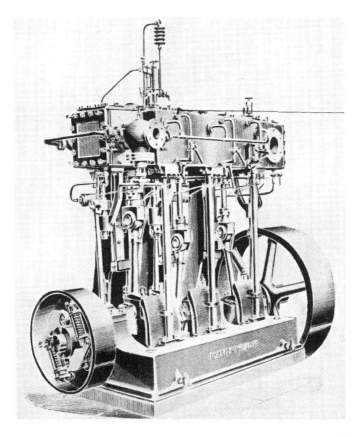

valves. This gear comprises two Cornish equilibrium valves, one at each end of the cylinder, and lifted alternately by a fixed eccentric, thus giving a constant lead. The point of release, i.e. the cut-off, is regulated by the governor and is therefore proportional to the load. Corliss exhaust valves are placed beneath the cylinder, having a large opening combined with a short travel. Another large horizontal with positive valves and a cylinder 34 in. by 60 in. is included in Figure 95, which shows the complete engine on temporary foundations in the erecting shop.

A picturesque type of Robey engine is the Wall Engine which was once in fair demand and described by the makers as "a very convenient and economical form of motor for driving shafting in factories and Workshops". Being self-contained, as seen in Figure 96, they were bolted to a wall of the shop at any convenient height. The length of shafting on either side was flanged coupled direct to the engine crankshaft, and thus the necessity and expense of belting, gearing or other drive was dispensed with. There were two valves to each cylinder and the governor operated the expansion valve, thereby governing on the cut-off. It is interesting to note that the list price in the early 1900s of an 8 N.H.P. wall engine having duplex cylinders 7 in. by 12 in. was £108.

Very many manufacturers tackled the handy undertype engine and Robey & Co. Ltd. were no exception. In Figure 97 we have a view of the 40 N.H.P. size after completion in the

FIGURE 94. Robey's horizontal engine Class E

FIGURE 95. Robey horizontal engine with positive valves

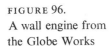

FIGURE 96.
A wall engine from
the Globe Works

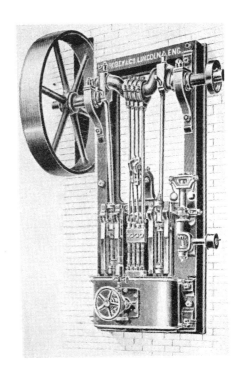

FIGURE 97. A fine Robey undertype

FIGURE 98. *Right:*
The Robey uniflow in undertype form

erecting shop. This had cylinders 12 in. and 21 in. by 24 in., ran at 100 R.P.M. with steam at 140 P.S.I., and the general features are self-evident from the picture. Besides the form shown in Figure 97 they could be supplied with a single or duplex cylinders and with a jet condenser in front of the smoke-box, and in tandem with and operated by an extension of the low-pressure piston rod. The makers claim to have made their first compound engine in 1864 and, with the accumulated experience, they state these compound undertypes use less than two pounds of best Welsh coal per I.H.P. per hour. This economy is achieved by the steam from the H.P. being reheated in a receiver of large capacity, thus reducing heat losses to a minimum. These engines were also renowned for their steady running and were much in vogue for driving electric generators a decade ago, and it is interesting to note in passing that a Robey undertype drove the dynamo for the first electric light in Cleethorpes in 1882.

Another particularly interesting variation on the undertype theme is the Robey Uniflow Undertype depicted in Figure 98.

FIGURE 99. A Robey traction engine under test
in the works yard

FIGURE 100. The Robey 5-ton steam motor tractor

Admission is by a spring-loaded poppet valve on top of each end of the cylinder, the central exhaust being via a trunk cast round the centre of the cylinder and thence to the condenser, as seen in the illustration. Apart from the crosshead the remainder of the motion was totally enclosed.

The Robey Uniflow is also made as a large and separate horizontal engine known as the Class ES, and these have a number of advantages, viz. a high vacuum due to the large opening to exhaust, a high efficiency and economy in steam consumption, simplicity in construction with a consequential smaller floor space required, and good accessibility and forced lubrication to all parts. Arising out of the last, there is the factor of less maintenance required. In addition, with the excellent governing entirely on a very early cut-off, they show a very high steam economy at partial loads. A combined centrifugal and inertia type of shaft governor is mounted on the layshaft and regulates the speed within very fine limits. In view of the simplicity of the Uniflow compared with, say, a comparable quadruple expansion engine, and the known advantages, it is a source of wonder to the writer that the Uniflow engine has not been more widely adopted and used.

After the turn of the century the traction engine had been developed into the fine machine depicted in Figure 99, which illustrates the double-crank compound engine of 6 N.H.P. on test in the work's yard. These compound machines worked at 180 P.S.I., were of the four-shaft layout and were made in 5, 6, 7, 8 and 10 N.H.P. sizes, that shown in Figure 99 having cylinders 6 in. and 10 in. by 12 in. There was also a similar range of single-cylinder machines working at 150 P.S.I., the 10 N.H.P. engine having a cylinder 10 in. by 12 in.

Besides the traction engines there was the 5-ton steam motor tractor depicted in Figure 100, which, similar to those by other makers, worked at 200 P.S.I. The compound cylinders were 5 in. and $8\frac{1}{4}$ in. by 9 in. and developed 18–20 B.H.P. at 200 R.P.M. Later engines could be supplied shod with solid rubber tyres.

An extremely interesting Robey self-moving road engine is the Tandem Roller shown in Figure 101, having a small quick-reverse two-crank compound engine mounted on top of a loco-

FIGURE 101. Quick-reverse Robey tandem roller

type boiler with round firebox and without stays, and pressed to 200 P.S.I. The crankshaft runs in ball bearings while the second motion shaft is really a stub axle (on the L.H.S.) on which the gears rotate, and final drive is by pitch chain to the hind axle. A number of these are yet in regular use. The quick-reverse principle was also applied to an orthodox three-wheeler roller known as the *Lion* road roller, which could be fitted with a three-tyne scarifier.

One of the most famous Robey products is the wagon, and one of the latest, mounted on pneumatic tyres and with the motion enclosed, is reproduced in Figure 102. The engine and boiler were a similar unit to that used in the quick-reverse tandem roller, but in this instance the boiler works at 250 P.S.I. Three speeds are used in the gearing on the crankshaft and stub countershaft, the final drive being by pitch chain with a differential within the large driven chain wheel on the rear axle.

Being still in demand the present-day Robey portable has been altered in some measure, the most noteworthy alteration being in the road wheels, now fabricated from steel plate as seen in Figure 103, illustrating one rated at 42 E.H.P., and

98

FIGURE 102. The Robey wagon on pneumatic tyres

FIGURE 103. The latest Robey portable still in production

having a single cylinder 10½ in. by 14 in. It is interesting to note that although these engines incorporate a number of new features in keeping with recent developments in production, Salter safety valves are still used as being the most suitable. They are also supplied in duplex and compound forms, the working pressures being 150, 120 and 160 p.s.i. for the single cylinder, duplex and compound types respectively.

The Globe Works are one of probably only three establishments in the county, and incidentally one of very few in the whole country, who produce steam engines today, the types in current production including Uniflow; Long Stroke Horizontals with either Drop, Positive, Piston, Corliss or Slide Valves; High Speed Vertical; Portable and Semi-Portable (including the Superheated example). The larger horizontals are rated up to 80 B.H.P. with a single cylinder and the duplex and compounds up to 170 and 128 B.H.P. respectively. In the vertical high-speed type sizes range up to 50 B.H.P. for a single cylinder and up to 500 B.H.P. with compound cylinders. The superheated semi-portable can be obtained up to 350 B.H.P. and the ordinary portable and semi-portable up to 120 B.H.P.

XXVI. RUSTON & HORNSBY LTD.
Sheaf Iron Works, Lincoln.

Established in 1840 as Proctor & Burton with premises at Waterside South and by 1849 were classified as "Millwrights & Engineers". Shortly afterwards they were styled Burton & Proctor and when Joseph Ruston entered into the partnership in 1857 the new title was Ruston, Proctor & Co., becoming Ruston, Proctor & Co. Ltd. in 1899. As such they continued until the amalgamation with Richard Hornsby & Sons Ltd. (see No. XVIII) in 1918, when the famous Ruston & Hornsby Ltd. came into being. In 1940 they entered into an association with Davey, Paxman & Co. Ltd. of Colchester. In 1885 the works covered thirteen acres. Frank Ruston, nephew of Joseph Ruston, served his time at Lincoln and afterwards became the partner in Armitage & Ruston, Honeysome Road, Chatteris, Cambridgeshire.

In the early days the portable engine was made in some numbers and Figure 104 depicts an example of the period 1875–90,

FIGURE 104. Single-cylinder portable engine by
Ruston, Proctor & Co. Ltd.

although they were also made with duplex cylinders. The single
cylinder was known as Class PS and the duplex as Class PD.
The range in Class PS was from 2½ to 12 N.H.P. (cylinders
5¼ in. by 9 in. to 12 in. by 15 in.) and in Class PD from 8 to 30
N.H.P. (cylinders two 6¼ in. by 12 in. and two 13 in. by 18 in.),
with a working pressure of 80 P.S.I. A special boiler having a
removable firebox and tubes could also be supplied "in which
by unscrewing the nuts round the front plate, and others
securing the tubeplate in the smokebox, the furnace with the
tubes and front tubeplate can all be withdrawn together from
the Boiler. . . .".

The firm's first traction engine appeared in 1876 and a representative example of this period is seen in Figure 105. They
were all three-shaft engines, the front axle was set well aft of
the smokebox and note that the cylinder is tied to the horn-
plates by a circular tie, as in certain portable engine practice.
With a single cylinder the range included 6, 7, 8 and 10 N.H.P.

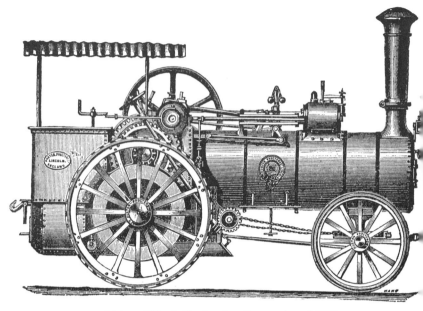

FIGURE 105. A Ruston traction engine of 1876

FIGURE 106. Small 0–4–0 contractor's locomotive by Rustons

102

FIGURE 107. Ruston locomotive for the G.E.R. in 1868

sizes and duplex cylinders could also be supplied for the 8 and
10 N.H.P. machines.

Besides road engines, railway locomotives were made in
small numbers, two types of which were for contractors' use,
and one of them is illustrated in Figure 106. Having the 0–4–0
wheel arrangement on a 5 ft. wheelbase they were eminently
suitable for sharp curves. The two cylinders were 9 in. by 16 in.,
wheels 2 ft. 9 in. dia. and a total heating surface of 275 sq. ft.
Note that the saddle tank is placed well forward over the boiler
and in this position it served to balance the overhang at the
rear end; consequently, these engines ran remarkably smoothly.
They were first produced in 1867–8.

Subsequently, the type was modified to have cylinders 10 in.
by 16 in., less rear overhang and a spectacle plate with rear-
wards roof extension. A number of these small locomotives
were supplied to the Manchester Ship Canal Works.

Perhaps the most famous Ruston railway locomotives were
their 0–6–0 side-tank jobs, five of which were supplied to the
G.E.R. in 1868, of which one lasted until 1951. They had
cylinders 16 in. by 22 in., coupled wheels 4 ft. dia., and their
general outline is shown in Figure 107. Three were fitted in

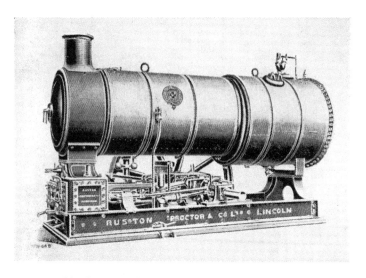

FIGURE 108. Compound undertype by Ruston, Proctor & Co. Ltd.

1891–3 with three-ton jib cranes and in this guise spent their time usefully in the precincts of Stratford Works. Others of the type were supplied to the War Office.

Both overtype and undertype engines were made in very many sizes, the former being in effect the portable engine without wheels or axles. The undertypes were erected usually on girder frames and the most interesting form is illustrated in Figure 108, which depicts the compound engine steamed by a boiler having the firm's removable firebox and tubes and known as Class GR. The N.H.P.s range from 6 (cylinders 5 in. and 8 in. by 10 in.) to 50 (cylinders 14 in. and 22½ in. by 24 in.), at speeds of 250 and 90 R.P.M. respectively, the working pressure being 120 P.S.I. in all cases.

Several forms of horizontal engines were always listed and a typical example known as the Class B is seen in Figure 109, having a single cylinder lagged with mahogany, a disc crank overhung and variable expansion valves to all in the range. The smallest had a cylinder 8 in. by 16 in. and the largest one of 27 in. by 52 in., of which the makers were justly proud and

FIGURE 109. Ruston, Proctor Class B horizontal engine

said of them, "The Engine is of a most massive pattern, and singularly rigid in work; its durability being thereby increased, the slight extra outlay over an inferior machine is soon repaid". Other types of horizontals comprised two engines of the Class B range, cross-coupled and each having its own stop-valve, two-crank compound machines erected on a girder frame, and also two-crank compound engines complete with Corliss valve gear to the H.P., with the usual eccentric and slide valve to the L.P. These were known as the Class LC engines. Single-cylinder engines with Corliss valves were also supplied, and also with two cylinders arranged on the cross-coupled principle, and a good example of the latter is depicted in Figure 110. It will be noted what picturesque machines they are and it need hardly be added that they are most interesting to watch at work.

A derivative from the horizontal engines were the various types of winding engines of which no less than nine types were made. A fine representative example is the Class WDC engine depicted in Figure 111, having direct-acting cross-coupled Corliss cylinders, two drums fitted with clutches and all worked

FIGURE 110. Picturesque cross-coupled compound
Ruston engine with Corliss valves

FIGURE 111. A direct-acting Ruston winding engine

at 120 P.S.I. The largest had cylinders 18 in. by 42 in. Figure
111 shows a corner view from which all the main details are
apparent. Other types of winding engines included were cross-
coupled geared winders with slide valves, cross-coupled and
direct-acting with Stephenson's link motion, small geared
hoists driven by single-cylinder vertical engine and vertical
boiler all mounted on four road wheels, duplex high-pressure

106

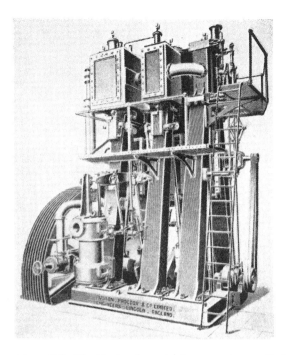

FIGURE 112. The Ruston large triple-expansion vertical
engine Class TX

winders with single spur gear to the drums and several other types.

Vertical engines of all types were at one time in production and included high-speed totally-enclosed machines having single and compound cylinders, open types with similar cylinders and a large and fine triple expansion condensing job depicted in Figure 112. Known as Class TX engines they were built in from 160 to 400 I.H.P. and all took steam at 160 P.S.I. Lastly there was the small and interesting little duplex engine adapted to drive by the gearing, as shown in Figure 113, a capstan on the deck above in the fishing smacks in which they were installed. Three sizes were made, known as Class TT, having duplex cylinders 4 in. by 8 in., 4½ in. by 8 in. and 5 in. by 8 in., and all used steam at 80 P.S.I.

107

FIGURE 113. Steam capstan by Ruston, Proctor & Co. Ltd.

FIGURE 114. Double-crank compound Ruston traction engine

FIGURE 115. Single-cylinder Ruston roller

Over the years the firm's traction engine had been developed and improved into the fine-looking machine seen in Figure 114, which illustrates the two-crank compound engine Class SC, with slide valves mounted on top of the cylinders and inclined, and four shafts in the transmission. Single-cylinder engines were also made in great numbers and a roller of this type is depicted in Figure 115. The common sizes were $10\frac{1}{2}$, $12\frac{1}{2}$ and 15 tons, the corresponding cylinder dimensions being 8 in. by 12 in., $8\frac{1}{2}$ in. by 12 in. and 9 in. by 12 in. respectively. They were known as Class SR machines.

In common with many other firms building self-moving engines Rustons produced the workmanlike 5-ton steam motor-tractor illustrated in Figure 116. Two-crank compound cylinders $4\frac{1}{2}$ in. and $7\frac{1}{2}$ in. by 9 in. were used, steam jacketed and taking steam at 180 P.S.I. Two speeds were incorporated in the cast-steel gearing, giving road speeds of $2\frac{1}{2}$ and 5 M.P.H., and a

109

FIGURE 116. Ruston's 5-ton steam motor tractor

FIGURE 117. A favourite Ruston product—the steam navvy

gross load of seven tons could be hauled up a hill of 1 in 10.
These little machines were known as the Class SCD engines.

One of the most world-famous Ruston products is their
steam navvy, of which various sizes and types were made, and
a typical example is included in Figure 117. All motions of
digging, slewing and moving were provided by either a duplex
horizontal engine mounted on the main chassis or a similar

110

vertical mounted on the side of the vertical boiler. As early as 1899, 205 of these navvies had been made and sold and it is undoubtedly the experience gained with their steam excavating machinery which has helped the firm to produce such a fine heavy-oil engine-driven range of excavators today.

The last steam engines were made in the Sheaf Iron Works in 1936.

XXVII. WILLIAM STEPHENSON & CO. LTD.
Holme Street, Great Grimsby.

In 1889 the title of this now defunct firm was Smith & Stephenson but by 1893 it had become as above and continued so until its demise in the early 1900s.

Their main product was a number of steam winches which were of the orthodox type of the period, having duplex cylinders, slide valves and Stephenson's link motion to each valve. They were usually fitted to fishing vessels and small coasters and there may be several still in use on boats frequenting the East Coast ports.

XXVIII. B. D. TAPLIN & CO.
Patent Crank Works, Lincoln.

Little appears to be known about this small and curious firm save that for a short spell in the early sixties they made one or two interesting traction engines. In 1863 Benjamin Dutton Taplin was one of the partners in Taplin & Glazier, at 264 High Street, Lincoln, "Physicians & Surgeons". Joseph and William Lee at one time resided at Humberstone Road, Leicester, but later the address of Joseph was "Traction Engine Works", Lincoln, so apparently the firm called their premises "Patent Crank Works" or "Traction Engine Works" as they pleased. Both the Lees were patentees and their most important patent (No. 947 of 1862) was in the name of Joseph. We have, therefore, the rare example of a member of the medical profession who was also a partner in an engineering concern. Such a strong combination should have lasted well, but unfortunately nothing has been forthcoming about them after *c.* 1865.

The main features of the above patent consisted of laying out the transmission in a traction engine so that the centres of

111

FIGURE 118. Taplin's interesting patent traction engine

the crankshaft, countershaft and rear axle were vertically in line one above the other. The countershaft consisted of a fixed stud and the gear wheel turned on it.

The engine as produced was shown at the Great Exhibition of 1862 and an engraving of one is reproduced in Figure 118. This curious machine was rated at 16 N.H.P.—a very high rating at this period—and the price was £590. It is described as a double-cylinder engine but a careful examination of the engraving shows only one set of eccentric rods, and the writer feels that what is reproduced is not the 16 but the firm's 12 N.H.P. engine of the same period and listed at £425. The cylinder is jacketed in the smokebox and steam was probably taken from the dome over the firebox via an internal pipe in the shell to the cylinder. This machine ran firebox first and steerage was effected by a handwheel and bevels as shown. Two speeds were provided by utilising a double spur ring on the driving wheel and two sliding pinions of suitable sizes on the end of the crankshaft. Although a coupling hook is provided at the rear or smokebox end, no similar attachment appears to be provided at the other end, which might be a handicap when manœuvring a threshing machine through an awkward gateway. Of these engines the makers said, "It is suitable for Government works, contractors at home and abroad, mill,

112

mine and quarry owners, or for any other purpose requiring immense steam power". Another interesting statement by B. D. Taplin & Co. was "Prices and particulars quoted for traction engines up to 50 horse-power", but whether brake or indicated horse power is not stated. Few of these engines appear to have been turned out and the author has been unable to contact any elderly Lincolnian who can remember seeing or hearing one at work in his extreme youth.

XXIX. WILLIAM TUXFORD & SONS
Boston & Skirbeck Ironworks, Boston.

William Wedd Tuxford was a man of extensive knowledge and a craftsman in wood and metal, and in 1824-5 (a very wet period for agriculture) he concentrated on the "reeing" of wheat and ultimately devised a machine for this process, protected by Patent No. 5954 of 1830. His family were flour dealers and bakers in Boston Market Place (Skirbeck parish adjoins Boston Town), and this fact accounts for his interest in grain and flour and why he constructed a tall and fine eight-sail windmill, with a workshop attached, close by Skirbeck church in 1826. A small local founder (name unknown) flatly declined to make castings for Mr. Tuxford for use in his newly evolved reeing machine, so, nothing daunted, the inventor decided to do the work in his own shop at the foot of the above windmill. Incidentally, Mr. Tuxford received financial help from Wilks, the great Reform M.P. for Boston, in the building of this mill, and in the election of 1832 his opponents dubbed it "Wilks Mill". Two years after the foundation of the engineering side of the Tuxford business, i.e. in 1828, W. W. Tuxford and his brother, Peter Tuxford, made the second trial bore for water in Boston Market Place on the west side, but after boring to a depth of 572 ft. the required amount of water was not obtained, although the bore had cost Mr. Wilks more than £2000. By 1838 William Tuxford had been joined by his two sons Weston and Wedd, the title of the firm now being Tuxford & Sons, as it remained until the close, the founder dying on 11 August 1871, in his ninetieth year. I am informed by an old Bostonian who joined a Spalding firm in 1883 as an apprentice that Tuxfords then supplied castings to them "for several

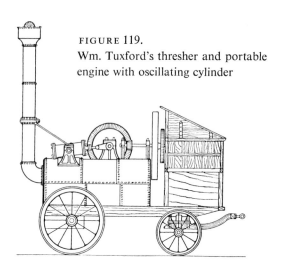

FIGURE 119.
Wm. Tuxford's thresher and portable
engine with oscillating cylinder

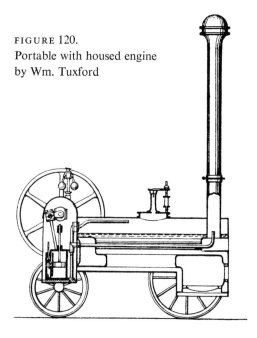

FIGURE 120.
Portable with housed engine
by Wm. Tuxford

years". Collitt & Co. (see No. VIII) succeeded to the premises and goodwill in 1887 and after a few years they too ceased to exist. The old works at Skirbeck still stand, used as a warehouse, and in the hey-day of "Tuxfords" extended over six acres. It was during the height of their activities that they illustrated a complete tower windmill in their catalogue along with an interesting array of engines.

It was in 1839 that two gentlemen, Mr. Wingate of Hareby and Mr. Morton, manager of Earl Ducies Whitfield Experimental Farm, suggested to Mr. Tuxford that he apply steam power to his own reeing and dressing machine, and a design, and even working models, of such a layout were prepared. But they were relegated to a shelf in the work's office at Skirbeck until 1842, when a full-size prototype was completed and which is illustrated in Figure 119. Note that the engine and threshing machine are mounted on one frame or chassis carried on four road wheels and with shafts for horse haulage. The engine has an oscillating cylinder on top of the boiler and the flywheel shaft runs at right angles to the crankshaft, being driven by bevel gearing, and it in turn drives the drum shaft of the thresher by spur gearing. A slide valve is fitted, operated only by the motion of the cylinder which would give a cut-off at the end of the stroke—not very economical. To offset this a copper exhaust-feed water-heater was included. The boiler is fired from the front end and is equipped with an oval return tube. Seven such sets were made, the first going to Mr. Robert Roslin of Algarkirk, after which twelve others, slightly modified, were also made. These complete units scaled $3\frac{1}{4}$ tons and the engines were rated at 6 N.H.P.

At Easter 1850 the firm completed the first of a new type of portable engine, always known as their "housed" engine because the engine portion was arranged vertically behind one end of the boiler and completely enclosed or housed in a sheet iron casing; a sectional view of a typical housed engine is seen in Figure 120. Both engine and boiler are particularly interesting, the former being of the Tuxford vertical side-rod type where the piston rod terminates in a wide crosshead, having attached to it two side rods connected to a block, one on either side of, and sliding in a groove cast in, each side of the cylinder

barrel. Fitted to the outside of these blocks are the two connecting rods proper, driving up to the single crank having a
very wide dip, carried in bearings mounted in the side casing.
These details are easily understood from the diagram in Figure
120. Referring again to Figure 120 it will be noticed that the
boiler is ingenious in shape, having the firebox at the front end
leading to a flattened oval flue extending to the far end of the
shell. This oval flue terminated in a double-bent end-plate and,
in addition, was fitted with a very long narrow cross-tube.
The dryback end-plate carried a nest of ordinary 5-ft.-long
tubes separated at their far end (i.e. the front end of the boiler
again) in a small smokebox, and note that the chimney was
inserted into it and passed through the steam space. An
inspection door was fixed to the top centre of the shell and
carried a spring-loaded safety valve. Although two inspection
doors were included in the back end-plate behind the engine,
and another at the front end for tube sweeping, these boilers
were always difficult to keep clean. They were, however, very
economical, and in 1855 at the R.A.S. Show at Carlisle their
coal consumption was as low as 3.75 pounds per horsepower
per hour. After 1855 the arrangement of the boiler was reversed,
i.e. the smoke tubes were at the bottom with the oval flue on
top, and in this guise their 8 N.H.P. engine returned only 3.5
pounds of coal per horse power per hour at the Worcester
Show in 1863—the last year in which these engines were made.

This side-rod design of engine was marketed in a stationary
vertical form illustrated in Figure 121, where the crankshaft,
with the necessary very wide dip, is mounted on an entablature
supported on four C.I. columns and all possessed of distinctive
architectural features. The base is plain and the cylinder is
mounted in the centre. When applied to a horizontal engine
the layout is as depicted in Figure 122, showing it coupled
vis-à-vis to a plunger pump and complete with large air vessel.
In this engine the cylinder measures $6\frac{1}{2}$ in. by 12 in., the ports
are of the "long" variety and cast all in one, whilst the grooves
on each side of the cylinder to take the slide blocks are of V
section, as are the blocks themselves. It is gratifying to record
that this interesting relic still exists in Cambridgeshire. Figures
121 and 122 should be studied together.

116

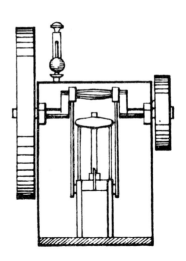

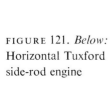

FIGURE 121. *Right:*
Tuxford's vertical side-rod
engine

FIGURE 121. *Below:*
Horizontal Tuxford
side-rod engine

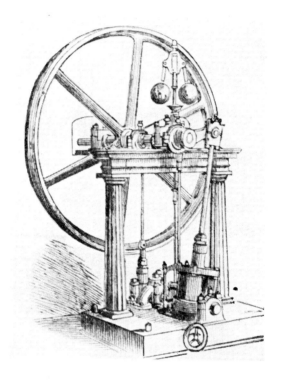

FIGURE 123. Semi-entablature engine by Wm. Tuxford

Another form of semi-entablature engine is seen in Figure 123, but here the cylinder is made oscillating, the second bearing to the crankshaft being placed in the adjacent wall and the drive taken from a pulley on the shaft end. These engines were fitted with a slide valve to give an early cut-off, an improvement over the end of the stroke cut-off incidental to when it is effected by the movement of the cylinder only.

Following the side-rod type of portable engine came the unusual "housed" engine depicted in Figure 124, where the cylinder was vertical, enclosed in a steam chest or jacket, and, as the makers put it, "the working parts are enclosed in an iron house at the end of the boiler, and are under lock and key".

FIGURE 124. Portable with cylinder under lock and key

The boiler could be supplied either with flues and tubes or in the ordinary locomotive form.

After the housed form of engine came the orthodox layout of portable engine included in Figure 125, which illustrates the firm's later type of 1½ N.H.P. machine—the smallest in the range, having a cylinder only 4¾ in. by 8 in. and now the author's property. Bearing the famous Tuxford nameplate in the form of a ring round the plug-type stop-valve it proclaims the work's number to be 1283. It is used when required and, needless to say, the writer never tires of revelling in the silence and power of the little engine, best apparent when belted to a circular saw. The range, of course, included much larger sizes

FIGURE 125. 1½ N.H.P. Tuxford portable engine in
the author's possession

up to 16 N.H.P., the last named having, in 1867, duplex
cylinders 8½ in. by 12 in. steam jacketed, and with an expansion
valve to each. The 4, 5, 6 and 8 N.H.P. engines had a single
cylinder 6 in. by 10 in., 6½ in. by 11 in., 7 in. by 12 in. and
8½ in. by 12 in. respectively.

Like many other famous mechanical firms, Tuxfords were
attracted to the self-moving engine, and as early as 1857 had
designed and made the interesting *Boydell* engine depicted in
Figure 126, examples of which were exported to the West
Indies and Cuba. Note that they were three-wheeled engines,
each wheel utilising Boydell's patent shoes attached to the
rim by cycloidal slotted links. The boiler was of the firm's
return-tube type with the favourite vertical side-rod engine

120

placed as it was in the portable engine, only in this instance duplex cylinders were used, the tops of the covers being easily discernible in Figure 126. Steerage by the one small front wheel was actuated by a ship's wheel mounted horizontally and with a pinion and gear wheel set below, thereby enabling the engine to be turned in a circle of only 30 feet diameter. The complete engine weighed 12 tons and the contemporary Press described it as "a sort of Leviathan, more powerful than the elephant and yet as manageable as the farmer's best-bred cart horse".

The steeple engine was another type manufactured at Skirbeck and a typical example is included in Figure 127, embellished with architectural details so apparent in the "cast-iron period". The cylinder is fixed vertically, the piston rod being triangular in form so as to embrace the crank and shaft which runs between and through the triangle formed of the rod. The crosshead is at the top, the guides for which constitute the steeple effect. Finally, the connecting rod transmits motion to the crank from the crosshead. The makers claimed that "It is handsome in appearance as well as economical, efficient and

FIGURE 126. The Tuxford-Boydell traction engine of 1857

FIGURE 127. Tuxford steeple engine with triangular connecting rod

simple and is strongly recommended". The standard sizes were 6, 8, 10 and 12 N.H.P., the respective cylinder bores being 8 in., 9 in., 10 in. and 11 in. The 6 N.H.P. was listed at £160 and the 12 N.H.P. at £250 in 1865.

Similar to the steeple engine is the Tuxford table engine, and the writer is fortunate in being able to illustrate an existing engine by the photograph reproduced in Figure 128, which shows the engine yet preserved in Soames Brewery, Spalding, and which once drove part of their plant. Note the long side-rods transmitting the drive from the crosshead to the wide crank placed below the table, the architectural features of the table and the delicate tracery embellishing the crosshead guides. Truly a poem in cast iron. This particular engine has a cylinder 8 in. by 16 in. and as a type they were turned out in 6, 8, 10 and 12 N.H.P. sizes.

It might not be out of place here to mention that the differentiation between a steeple and a table engine can always be made if it be remembered that in the steeple layout the crankshaft is between the crosshead and the cylinder; whilst the table engine has the cylinder between the crosshead and the crank.

As one would expect, the beam engine was another favourite

122

at this time and a typical early example is to be seen in Figure 129. Note the Watt parallel motion where the coupler is divided externally, and the details of the cast-iron connecting rod. Tuxfords were justly proud of this range and said of them, "They are finished with a metallic piston, a handsome set of governors and are in every respect complete". The range comprised engines of 10, 12, 16, 20 and 25 N.H.P., the list price of the last named being £550.

As might be anticipated, Tuxfords supplied beam engines for pumping in the surrounding fens, and in Figure 130 we have a view of a large and fine beam engine erected in Timberland

FIGURE 128. Tuxford table engine still existing

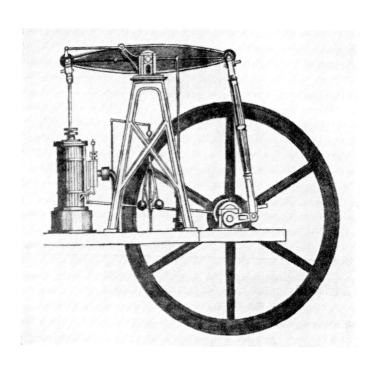

FIGURE 129. *Above:*
Small Tuxford beam
engine

FIGURE 130. *Left:*
Large Tuxford beam
engine formerly at
Timberland

124

FIGURE 131.
The Tuxford small
wall hoist

pumping station in 1854, but unfortunately ruthlessly destroyed
in 1926. It had a stroke of three feet, worked at 28 R.P.M. and
drove a scoop wheel.

Other steam prime movers completed at the works comprised
pile drivers and hoists and Figure 131 illustrates their hoist
with duplex cylinders, forked connecting rods, valve chest
between the cylinders and worm drive to the rope drum
mounted above. The whole is erected on a C.I. plate, drilled
for bolts along the edges for wall fixing. The example shown
in Figure 131 was existing in 1953.

For many years England has exported winding engines of all
types to all parts of the world and Tuxford & Sons were one of
the firms engaged in making one example of this form of steam

125

FIGURE 132. Large Tuxford winding and mining engine

engine, and their product is reproduced in Figure 132. Here
we have a large engine with duplex cylinders mounted on top
of a conventional type of locomotive boiler, with the refinement of lagging over all of the exterior of the firebox as well
as over the barrel. Salter safety valve, starting and slide valves
are all incorporated in the cylinder block, giving the engine a
very neat appearance. The winding drum is located as shown
and the drive is by a pinion on the end of the crankshaft
meshing with an internal-toothed annulus attached to the
drum back-plate. This back-plate was keyed to the countershaft
but was only connected to the drum proper (free on the countershaft) by a friction ring pressed on to the end of the drum by
the foot pedal seen near the ashpan. Besides the winding drum
was the plunger pump rod of trussed timber construction,
worked off the disc right on the end of the countershaft. This
disc and its boss were also free on the countershaft but could
be engaged by means of a dog-clutch operated by the horizontal hand-lever as shown. By this ingenious layout it was
possible to run the pump or winding drum together or separately as desired, and there was also a free engine position. The
cranks were set at 90° and the flywheel was on the right-hand
side.

126

Reverting to the firm's self-moving engines the successor to the *Boydell* is included in Figure 133, and here again the two vertical cylinders, housed as before, are retained, although the layout of the rest of the machine is quite different. The rear of the chassis is formed of a dicky-seat to carry three persons, the crew being in front, and the drive to the single rear driving wheel was by gearing. Water was carried in the large underslung tank. William Tuxford claimed that "It steers readily and is managed easily", and he classified it as a road locomotive. They were made in three sizes of 8, 10 and 12 N.H.P., the last being listed at £500 in 1862.

The customer had the option of having one cylinder with an ordinary locomotive boiler and this alternative type was made in two sizes only of 8 and 10 N.H.P.

Another self-moving engine of this period is seen in Figure 134 with four wheels and a single vertical cylinder. It incorporated the famous return-tube design of boiler, the manstand

FIGURE 133. Tuxford traction engine-cum-carriage
to carry three persons

FIGURE 134. Tuxford road engine with single cylinder

FIGURE 135. Tuxford traction engine with front truck

128

FIGURE 136. Later type Tuxford traction engine at Syston in 1914

being in front with front-wheel steerage and independent front-wheel suspension. Note too the water tank slung beneath the boiler and chimney with spark arrester.

A year later the design had been altered to chain transmission, utilising a countershaft beneath the boiler but with the now orthodox horizontal cylinder and motion where the cylinder is mounted over the back end. The crew were accommodated in a separate truck bolted to the front end and all wheels were mounted on rubber springs. A side view is included in Figure 135.

By 1871 many more improvements had been adopted and a normal form of locomotive-type boiler formed the basis of the engine which is illustrated in Figure 136. The chain and countershaft drive are still retained but the water-tank is fashioned in a downwards extension of the smokebox, the fore-carriage accommodating the fuel, housing the worm-and-quadrant steering and the crew. Incidentally, this grand old engine worked at Syston until 1914.

The final form of the chain-cum-countershaft engines is seen in the diagram reproduced in Figure 137. The cylinder, 9 in. by 12 in., is mounted on the boiler in the usual place but the whole of the front end is carried on the pair of driving

129

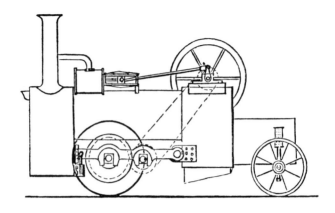

FIGURE 137. Spring-mounted Tuxford light traction engine

FIGURE 138. Another late type traction engine by
Wm. Tuxford & Sons

wheels mounted along with the adjacent countershaft, in side-plate frames. At the firebox end these frames are hinged to small side-plates, but at the front end the frames are strengthened by an angle iron cleat to each, the end of the engine being suspended from them by two rods, one on each side bearing on rubber pads on springs mounted in c.i. boxes to house them. The tender is also spring mounted but on a different principle as the stub axles are forged on to vertical rods which can slide in brackets riveted to the side of the tender, the rods being controlled by the helical steel springs compressed in the brackets. The crankshaft was geared 2 to 1 down to the countershaft, the final drive providing a further reduction of 6 to 1, so that the overall ratio was 12 to 1.

Figure 138 shows the last type of traction engine made, many of which worked in this county for many years. Note the short wheelbase and the independent springing for the front wheels. The large jacketed cylinder is 9 in. by 12 in. and the gearing for the drive is on the usual right-hand side. A modified form of the early steerage is still retained, the wheel being in the manstand, the connection to the front wheels being by chain around the lower wheel (beneath the floor), terminating in two long rods one to each axle. The steersman maintained a straight course by keeping the outside edge of the flywheel in line with the inside edge of the nearside front wheel.

Few were the engine builders who did not make the familiar horizontal engine, and the Tuxford example is particularly neat and is illustrated in Figure 139. The starting valve is placed just above and to the left of the slide valve in the valve chest, the near side of the cylinder being neat and plain and lagged with polished strip mahogany. A boiler feed pump is bolted to the bedplate as shown and the rest of the engine is simple, straightforward and reliable. One such worked for many years in the woad mill at Algarkirk, near Boston. These engines were made in a variety of sizes and the necessary Cornish boiler could also be made and supplied.

Although my readers may have gathered from my *Steam-Engine Builders of Norfolk* that the power-driven roundabout originated in Norfolk by S. G. Soame and later and improved by Frederick Savage, the monopoly was by no means enjoyed

FIGURE 139. Tuxford's neat horizontal engine

by the maker in Lynn, for a very interesting set of gallopers was made in the Skirbeck Ironworks and is seen in Figure 140. The motive power took the form of a small engine with duplex cylinders and motion mounted on an ordinary locomotive-type boiler. The centre pole served also as the chimney and the canvas top or awning could be rolled back in sunny weather. It was made for the Boston Riding School Ltd. in 1878 who had offices in the town. In Figure 140 it is shown fully erected in the local park on the occasion of its first public trial.

Portable engines also appear to have been made right up to the close in 1887 and although the later engines left the works maroon colour, the earlier ones were finished a royal blue and very handsome they must have looked.

XXX. WILKINSON, WRIGHT & CO.
Grand Sluice Works, Boston.

It is uncertain when this very small firm commenced business but it was probably some years before 1860. By 1863 it was plain Henry Wright, well known as a maker of agricultural implements, and as such he continued in business until shortly after 1876. It appears that Wilkinson dropped out c. 1862.

They were makers of portable engines for a few years prior to the Great Exhibition of 1862 and on that occasion exhibited the good-looking portable engine depicted in Figure 141.

132

FIGURE 140. Tuxford's roundabout complete with centre engine

FIGURE 141. A good design of portable engine
by Wilkinson, Wright & Co.

Apparently it was the only size made, namely, 7 N.H.P., with the single cylinder heavily ribbed and one very unusual feature, i.e. the crosshead guides consisted of two circular bars arranged side by side—not one over the other. The regulator was contained in the valve chest, the feed pump was fitted to the side of the smokebox, and a tie-rod connected the front axle to the firebox.

The Index

❖❖❖❖❖❖❖❖❖❖❖❖❖❖❖❖❖❖❖❖❖❖❖❖❖❖❖❖❖❖❖❖❖❖❖❖❖❖

NOTE. Names in italics are those of engines and ships.

Publication of *Steam-Engine Builders of Lincolnshire* has been facilitated by the generosity of the organisations or individuals who have subscribed to the book. Our grateful thanks go to all those listed below.

SUBCRIBERS

Harold Abbott, Lincoln

Dr. C.A. Allen,
International Stationary
Steam Engine Society

R.P. Almand, Edinburgh

Margaret Arbon, Gainsborough

Ayscoughfee Hall Museum

Roger J. Audis, Bardney

G.C. & J.E. Ayto, Old Somerby

Thomas Baines, Bardney

Paul Barnes, Grantham

B.M.J. Barton, Corby Glen

John Bassindale, Birmingham

J.C. Bateman, Hipperholme

Ronald H. Beacham, Bletchley

William Bee, Lincoln

Mark Bennet, Lincoln

Maurice Berrill, Edinburgh

Christopher Berry, Bourne

S.J. Betteridge, Lincoln

Maureen Birch, S.L.H.A.

Neville Birch, S.L.H.A. (Chairman)

Sq. Ldr Alan Birt, Bury-St-Edmunds

W.J. Bleasdale, Preston

Tore Blom, Sweden

R.E.M. Booty, Barton-On-Humber

John Boucher, Nottinghamshire

Colin Bowden, Bishop's Stortford

H.C. Bowen, Fetcham

David G. Bramford, Dembleby

W.A. Briggs, Knutsford

Derek Broughton, Lincoln

Anthony J. Brown, Leicester

John F. Brown, Weymouth

Richard Burdon, Lincoln

A.V. Burgess, Norwich

Graham A. Carpenter, N. Moreton

R.A. Carroll, Spalding

B.L. Chapman, Norwich

Jim & Sonya Clarke, Pershore

P.L. Clements, Newark

Alan Clothier, Whitley Bay

J.E. Clowes, Stoke-On-Trent

David S. Colvin, Bedford

John Cook, Kirkby-La-Thorpe

Tom D. Cook, Morton, Notts.

John Alan Cooke, Lincoln

C.P. Cooling, Sunderland

Dr. Jim Coombes, Brighton

Bob Cooper, Loughborough

John Cooper,
International Stationary
Steam Engine Society

Colin Copcutt, Leighton Buzzard

S.A. Corston, Lusby

Peter Coulls, Leamington Spa

Brian Crawford, Witney

Rachel Jane Credland, Martin

Stephen Croad, Hounslow

D. Crook, Maidenhead

John Cross, Chelmsford

Stanley Daniels, Stamford

D.I. Dawson, Orpington

John Day, Dorking

W.G.M. Dickinson, Uley, Glos.

John Dolphin, Northampton

P.R. Donovan, Cricklade

Robin Drury, Newark

Stephen R. Ellerington, Ashby,
Scunthorpe

Fred Felstead, Bourne

M.J. Firth, Southampton

David Fish, Hull

J. Fisher, Wyberton

John T. Fletcher, Winterton

Mike Ford, M.E. Engineering,
Lincoln

Raymond A. Fox, Bedworth

Jean Francis, Boston

M. Fraser, Leicester

J.M. Frisby-Boor, Bourne

Gainsborough & District
Heritage Association

G.R. Garnham, Lincoln

N.A. George, Lincoln

C.B. Gibson, Lincoln

G. Gibson, Lincoln

Ian Gibson, Pickering

R.J. Gillard, Chard

Leslie T. Goor, Digby

Alan E. Gratton, Boston

P.H. Green, Essex

Geoffrey G. Greetham, Osbournby

J.M. Gregory, Winchester

Robert C. Grimmer, Holt

J.A. Gunson, Spilsby

C. Haigh, Lincoln

Eric Hair, Streets & Co.

Eleanor Hall, Newlandrig

J.M. Hammond, Nottingham

Michael Hanna, Lincoln

Martin Hanson, Boston

Alexander Hayward, Drinkstone

Malcolm Haynes, Volunteer,
    Museum of Lincolnshire Life

Ben Headon, Hollycombe
    Steam Collection

C.M. Hemming, Egglescliffe

Heritage Trust of Lincolnshire

P.A.R. Herratt, Tewkesbury

R.J. Heugh, Boston

John Hewson, Grimsby

D.J. Hicks, Holbeach

Richard Hilliar, Peterborough

D. Hillman, Cardiff

K.S.G. Hinde, Cambridge

Keith Hooper, Street, Somerset

Roger Howlett, Lincoln

Michael Hudson, Waddington

Peter M. Hughes, Thurstonland

John L. Hume, North Somercotes

Lawrance Hurst, Bushey Heath

Brian Hutchings, Stapleford

Laurence Ince, Solihull

Alan Jeeves, Huddersfield

Dr. Barry Job,
    Newcastle-Under-Lyme

K.D. Johnson, Lincoln

R.L. Jubb, Gainsborough

Nick Kelly, Shoreham-By-Sea

M. Kenning & R. Johnson
    Wrangle Lincs. Oil Engine Club

J.Kingma, Netherlands

Jayne Knight, Lincoln

C. Lee, Lincoln

Martin Lee, Gaddesby

Mark Richard Leggott, Holland Fen

Chris Lester, S.L.H.A.

Lincolnshire County Library Service

Lincolnshire Film Archive

Stuart Lines, Chesham

Gordon Long, Dodford

S.F. Long, Billingborough

M.D. Longdon, Lincoln

Toby Lyons, Stansted

Michael Mackintosh,
    Hutton-Le-Hole

W.J. McDonald, Swineshead

Bernard Manterfield, Grantham

Alberta Markillie, Boston

J.R. Marshall, Nettleham

Chris Medley, Newton-On-Trent

Ray Millington, Australia

Peter J. Moore, Bloxholm

D.S. Morley, N.I.A.S.

G. Mott, Spilsby

V.E. Murphy, Lewisham

Museum of Lincolnshire Life

N.L. Musham, Scothern

B. Naylor, Ketton

E. Neatby, Rotherham

P.A. Neaverson, Newtown Linford

Newark Libraries

Newton, Lincoln

John Norris, Australia

P.F. North M.C.I.T., Exeter

Patrick A. Nott, Newport I.o.W.

Michael J. O'Connor, Croydon

Kevin A. Oliver, Basingstoke

Les Osbourne, Lincoln

Dr. D.M. Owen, Thimbleby

C.J. Page, Cregneash Village Folk
    Museum, Isle of Man

D.C. Palmer, Nottingham

D. Pantry, Haxey Carr

Pat Parker, Lincoln

Stuart Parker, Lincoln

Walter Denis Parker, Lowestoft

W.J.D. Parkhouse, Coleford

Bob Paterson, Morebattle

O.H.J. Pearcey, London

D.R. Pearson, Gainsborough

P.B. Peart, Winterton

J.M. Peet, Tattershall

G.I. Phillips, Lincoln

John Edward Philpott, Cardiff

D. Pierce, Anglo Machine Eng. Ltd.
Lincoln

C.A. Pinchbeck, Heckington

Helen Platts, Worcester

M.A. Poole, Pulborough

N.R. Portass, Milton Keynes

P.R. Purcell, Corby

Mrs. K.M. Raisen, Frithville

Robert Reed, Duffield

J.F.T. Revey, Washingborough

H.L. Roberts, Spilsby

D.N. Robinson, Louth

Alwyn Rogers, Burnley

Janet Rowland,
Hollycombe Steam Collection

T.G. Rushby, Castleford

Alan Rust,
Lincoln Engineering Society

W.D. Ryan, Preston

J.C. Sawtell, B.I.A.S.

M. Searby, Holbeach

J.E. Searing, Wickford

J.A. Selby, Royal Leamington Spa

Ray Sellers, Staines

C.P. Sharp, Maulden, Bedford

Mary & Brian Shaw, Leeds

Noel Shelley & Catherine Armitage,
Ringstead Foundry

Mark Sissons, Market Bosworth

A.B. Smalley, Filton

Alan Smith, Washingborough

Alan G. Smith, Upper Cumberworth

Boyce Smith, Skegness

J.B. Smith, Starbeck, Harrogate

J.D. Smith, Newton Longville

Laurence G. Smith, Norfolk

Neil Smith, Misterton

R.T. Smith, West Drayton

P. Snusher, Lincoln

P.W. Spalding, Grantham

Stewart Squires, North Hykeham

William Starling, Stoke Holy Cross

David Start, Lincoln

W.N. Stone, Newcomen Society

Alan Stoyel, Stanford-in-the-Vale

B. Sullivan, S.L.H.A.

Dr. J. Suter, Leeds

W. Sumner, Stockport

Geoff Swain, Blidworth

Peter Taylor, Lincoln

David Thompson, Lincoln

David J. Threlfall, Freckleton

L.F. Tucker, Loughton

Paul H. Vigor, M.Soc.Sc (Ind.Arch)
Lymington

Keith M. Vigus B.D.S., Winscombe

Alan Walker, Lincoln

Paul Walkinshaw, Deeping St. James

A.C.L. Wall, S.L.H.A.

Derrick Warren, Taunton

James Waterfield, Maud Foster Mill

H.F. Watson, Grantham

Neil Watson, Boston

Pearl Wheatley, S.L.H.A.

Robin Wheeldon, Lincoln

Tim Wheeldon, Lincoln

Paul White, Lincoln

A.J. Wilkinson, Osgodby

David T. Wilkinson, Boston

Ben Wiltshire, Balderton

Brian Wood, Norwich

Norman Woolidge, Blackheath

A.W. Wright, Seaford

Neil & Sarah Wright, Lincoln

Alan Yarnell, Saxilby

Markus Zieglar, Switzerland